"It isn't easy for a
girl to refuse you."

Jake's response to Stacy's comment
came quickly. "That's because I don't
intend to have you refuse me," he
said. "I'm patient; I can wait for the
right moment."

"And if there isn't one?" Stacy
murmured.

"Then I'll make one." His dark head
lowered slowly and his lips took
possession of hers in a kiss of
languorous passion, a deliberate
onslaught to break down any barriers
she might have against him.

She had known this man only a
matter of hours! And yet she couldn't
hold back her response, couldn't
deny his effect on her.

Finally she pulled away from him, her
head dizzy with emotions. This
couldn't be happening to her, she
thought. Surely people didn't fall in
love so easily!

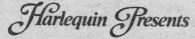

CAROLE MORTIMER

brand of possession

Harlequin Books

TORONTO • LONDON • LOS ANGELES • AMSTERDAM
SYDNEY • HAMBURG • PARIS • STOCKHOLM • ATHENS • TOKYO

Harlequin Presents edition published January 1981
ISBN 0-373-10406-5

Original hardcover edition published in 1980
by Mills & Boon Limited

CHAPTER ONE

"YOU CAN KEEP your job!" Green eyes blazed at the man sitting behind the desk. "I don't sell myself for any price."

"Miss Adams, if you will just calm down I will—"

"You won't do anything," Stacy interrupted angrily. "You're just as weak as the rest of them. Whatever Paul Forbes decides he wants he has to have, and woe betide the poor girl if she isn't interested. Keep the star of your film happy at any price, that's your motto. Well, here's one girl who isn't going to keep him happy. I loathe the man!"

"Miss Adams! You have completely the wrong impression of what I was trying to say. Mr. Forbes merely expressed a wish—"

"I'm well aware of what he wanted, Mr. Payne, and he isn't getting it from me. As the director of this film you should have better control over your actors."

"Now you've gone too far!" The little man rose indignantly to his feet. "You have a part that lasts about fifteen minutes of the film and you think that gives you the experience to tell me how to do my job. I've been directing films and placating actors for thirty years and I—"

"Then perhaps it's time you had a rest," Stacy told him rudely, her green eyes flashing, her long red tresses like fire down her back, softly waving down to her slender waist. She was still wearing the costume for her part in the film, the garb of a seventeenth-century peasant girl in rugged Cornwall. "Things have changed since you started out," she continued angrily. "The casting is no longer carried out on the studio couch."

"Miss Adams, you're fired!" His face had reddened almost to bursting point.

"Don't worry, I'm going. I like the part of Kate, but I'm not willing to sleep with Paul Forbes to keep it."

"I asked you to go to a party with him, not to go to bed with him." The director sighed. "I don't know why you have to read so much into a simple invitation—"

"If it's so simple why didn't he make it himself?" she challenged.

"I understand that he did—and you turned him down."

"Because I don't like him!" Stacy said fiercely. "I've seen him in action the last couple of weeks, and he's nothing but an egotistical, pompous, overbearing—"

"That's quite enough, Miss Adams," he told her coldly. "I think you have made your feelings concerning Mr. Forbes very clear. And I think I have made my feelings about your future employment here equally clear."

"Oh, you have. Don't worry, I'll leave. I think the rape scene I have to go through with him could turn out to be too realistic."

Martin Payne shifted some papers around on his desk. "Your cards and money will be ready for you first thing in the morning."

"Not earlier?" she sneered. "I would have thought you would have wanted me away from here as soon as possible."

"That isn't possible, I'm afraid. It's after five now and what meager office staff we have down here will have returned to their hotel for the evening."

"To get ready for the party this evening."

He nodded. "Exactly. The party you have refused to attend."

If the poor man thought she wasn't going to be there tonight he had another think coming. She had every intention of going—and with a partner of her own choosing. But she wasn't about to tell him that; he might try to prevent her. After all, it would be a slap in the face for Paul Forbes when she turned up with someone else. But it was a slap in the face she knew she would never physically be allowed to administer.

"Then I suppose the morning will have to do," she accepted with little grace, marching to the door of the caravan that passed as the director's office while they were on location. "Good night, Mr. Payne."

"Good*bye*, Miss Adams," he answered pointedly.

She gave him an impudent grin. "Oh, surely not goodbye, Mr. Payne. After all, I have to wait until tomorrow before I can leave."

"I doubt we will meet again, Miss Adams," he said in a stilted voice.

She left the caravan with a defiant flick of her head, an amused curve to her full mouth. Mr. Payne was right, most of the staff had already left, but there was still some of the cast left. Matthew Day was one of them, and he had been a good friend of hers for the past three years. She linked arms with him as they walked over to his car to drive back to the hotel.

Matthew was tall, dark and rugged, very handsome, and making quite a name for himself in films and television. Stacy had no doubt that within a couple of years Matthew would be landing leading roles in major films, but for the moment he only had a supporting role like herself—like she *had* had.

"You're looking pleased with yourself," he remarked on the way back to the hotel.

"I've been sacked!"

His foot momentarily jerked on the accelerator. "You've been *what*?"

"Sacked," she repeated happily.

"But why? And why do you look so happy about it? I thought this job meant a lot to you. The part of Kate may not be a large one, but it is a crucial one."

"I've been sacked because of Paul Forbes. He's decided that I attract him now."

"God, that man's incredible," Matthew exclaimed. "Last week it was Jan in makeup, the week before that Cindy Davies, the young kid playing his sister in the film. And now you. I take it you refused to play his little game?"

"Yes, and so he went straight to Payne and used all his egotistical power to try to get me to change my mind."

"Which you didn't," he stated knowingly.

"Did you expect me to?"

"No." He grinned ruefully. "I have firsthand experience of your moral principles."

"I thought you got over that long ago." The two of them had dated for a few months a couple of years ago, but they had finally decided to end things when it became apparent that they wanted different things from the relationship. Luckily they had managed to remain friends.

Matthew squeezed one of her hands as it lay in her lap. "I did, Stacy," he assured her. "I was only teasing you. But if Forbes got you the sack, why are you looking so pleased?"

"Because Paul Forbes wanted to take me to the party tonight being given for Jake Weston's arrival, and I'm going to enjoy turning up there with you."

"You mean you're still going, even after being sacked?"

"Definitely. I may not have been too enthusiastic about going in the first place—people fawning all over the author of this film isn't exactly my idea of a fun evening—but I'm definitely going now." She smiled with glee. "I wouldn't miss it for the world."

Matthew accepted her determination with a smile, knowing that once Stacy made her mind up about something, she very rarely changed it. "I'm quite looking forward to meeting the famous Jake Weston."

"You don't think the lowly workers like us will get an introduction, do you," she scoffed. "Goodness, you're expecting a lot."

"Why shouldn't we?" He drove the car into the huge hotel parking lot. Most of the hotel was full even though it was almost out of season. The film crew had more or less taken over the large hotel, any other guests finding it strange to be invaded with actors and all the technical staff that went with the making of a film. "We have as much right to meet him as anyone else."

"A man constantly on top of the best-seller list, every book he writes turned into a major film?" She shook her head. "He won't be interested in the lowlies like us. Besides, I've heard he isn't all that sociable."

"If he can attend a party of this size he has to be."

"Mm." Stacy got out of the car. "Well, I'm not at all interested in meeting him. He's probably one of those brash Americans who wears loud clothes and calls everyone 'buddy.'"

Matthew laughed, locking the doors to his blue sports car. "You shouldn't generalize. He could turn out to be tall, dark and handsome."

"Like you?" she teased. "No, I picture him as being short and fat, probably balding, and in his mid-forties," she said thoughtfully.

"Now I know you're wrong about his age—he's thirty-eight."

She wrinkled her nose. "Well, that's almost forty."

They had entered the hotel now, the receptionist giving them both a glowing smile as they walked over to the elevator. It was all very exciting having all these actors staying here, meeting people she had only ever seen on the television or in the movies.

Matthew chuckled. "I don't think people of thirty-eight would agree with you."

"Maybe not," she agreed, lowering her voice slightly as someone came to stand behind them. "But he's still twice my age, that makes him old."

"Poor devil," Matthew murmured. "Do you fancy a drink before dinner?"

She shook her head. "No, thanks, it's a bit early for me. Besides—" she looked down ruefully at the costume she was still wearing "—I think I should get out of this before I get accused of stealing it."

He laughed. "Okay, I'll see you later at dinner. And try not to be rude to our fat, balding, aging author tonight. I don't want you upsetting anyone else to do with the film—I still have to work here."

"Don't worry, like I told you, Jake Weston won't be interested in us," she stepped into the elevator, moving aside to allow the man standing behind them to enter, too. "And I promise to be on my best behavior."

Matthew grimaced. "You wouldn't know how."

She gave him a cheeky grin as the elevator doors swished shut, giving the man at her side, the only other occupant, a casual lookover. She instantly did a retake. Wow! Now here was a good example of someone tall, dark and handsome—and she felt sure this individual wasn't Jake Weston.

Stacy had never seen him before, but with those looks she felt he should have been starring in the film instead of Paul Forbes. He was gorgeous, although the dark scowl on his face gave him a slightly satanic look. He had jet-black hair, worn long over his collar but styled, piercing deep blue eyes, a high-bridged nose, and a strong firm mouth that hinted at a steely determination, and gave an impression that this man always got what he went after. He was very tall, well over six feet, his wide powerful shoulders tapering down to a narrow waist and firm muscular thighs, all shown to advantage in the black turtlenecked sweater he wore and the fitted black pants. Stacy guessed his age to be somewhere between thirty-five and forty.

She cleared her throat before attempting to talk. "Which floor?" she squeaked, her usually bubbly nature completely overwhelmed by his blatant magnetism.

He looked at her for the first time, those deep blue eyes running coolly over her appearance. "I beg your pardon?" he drawled, obviously not welcoming this intrusion into his thoughts.

Stacy hadn't missed the faint Atlantic drawl to his voice, the tone and sound very attractive. She hesitated with her finger on the elevator button. "Which floor would you like?" she explained.

"Oh." He nodded. "The top, please."

She couldn't help the slight rise of her eyebrows. The top floor contained the luxury suites of the hotel, reserved for the more wealthy guests. Adding two and two together, namely his American accent and the top-floor suite, she would hazard a guess on this man being an employee of Jake Weston.

She pressed the button for her own floor and then lightly touched the top button for her silent companion. She could smell the masculine odor of his after-shave, and her nose twitched appreciatively.

Not normally a reserved type of person, she found the silence between herself and this attractive man slightly irksome. Finally she couldn't stand it any longer, and turning to look at him, she found herself being thoroughly appraised by deep blue eyes. Her breath caught and her face flamed at the totally sexual assessment of that steady gaze. She turned hurriedly away, regretting her impulse to talk to him. She was used to causing some reaction in members of the opposite sex, but never anything this blatant.

"I take it you're working on the film?"

Stacy turned sharply at the sound of that deep, attractive voice. "Sorry?"

"By your costume I presume you're working on the film," he repeated.

She looked down ruefully at her revealed curves in the low neckline of the dress she wore, her face flaming with color as she realized this was probably the reason he had been staring at her and not because he found her attractive. He may only be an employee of Jake Weston, but she felt sure he wouldn't be interested in a young actress who was only just beginning to make a name for herself—*had* been; now that she had been sacked she didn't know what her next job would be, *or* when.

She nodded. "I was."

Those blue eyes narrowed, the dark shadow on his chin evidence that he was one of those men who needed to shave twice a day. She felt sure he would have a thick matt of hair on his chest, too, his skin deeply tanned. She brought herself up with a start as she realized how intimate her thoughts of him had become.

"Was?" he echoed sharply.

Stacy was surprised by the intensity of his gaze. "I'm afraid so; I've been sacked," she answered abruptly.

"You play the part of Kate," he said slowly, thoughtfully.

"I did. Excuse me," she stepped out as the elevator doors swished open at her floor. She was surprised when the man followed her out, the elevator moving swiftly up to the top floor, completely empty. "This isn't your floor," she pointed out hurriedly, unnerved by his proximity.

"I know that." He took hold of her elbow as someone walked past them. "Shall we go to your room?"

She snatched her arm out of his grasp, startled by his words. "How dare you!" she gasped. "I may have spoken to you, but I certainly didn't—"

His mouth turned back mockingly. "I'm not so stupid that I think a polite conversation in the elevator entitles me to invite myself into your bed. I suggested we go to your room as a means of gaining privacy; we seem to be attracting quite a lot of attention standing here." As if to prove his point one of the porters walked by, turning back to stare at them curiously.

"Well, yes. But...why should we need privacy?" she asked sharply.

He looked even more impatient. "I want to know more about the reason for your being dismissed from the film."

Her green eyes widened. "Why? It has nothing to do with you."

"It may," he contradicted curtly.

"Just because you work for Jake Weston doesn't give you the right—"

His dark brows rose. "What makes you think I work for Jake Weston?"

She shrugged. "I, well, you do, don't you?"

"I may."

She nodded. "I thought so."

"Mm, well now that you know I'm not just a curious stranger, perhaps you wouldn't mind telling me the reason you were fired."

"But I would," she said stubbornly. "The reasons are private and need only be known to the director and myself."

Those blue eyes remained intent upon her. "I disagree with you. Don't you think Mr. Weston has the right to know the reasons, too?"

"Perhaps," she admitted grudgingly. "But you aren't Jake Weston."

He acknowledged this with a grim smile. "Perhaps not, but I could tell him."

Stacy almost had to bend back to look up at him, he being at least a foot taller than her, if not more. He made her feel small and feminine, as if she could easily be crushed in his muscular arms, and it was a feeling she found strangely pleasing. "Why should he be interested in the sacking of a girl playing a minor role in a film he wrote?"

His mouth tightened as if in anger. "Because although you consider him to be—now what was it—fat, bald and aging? Mm." He nodded at her flushed face. "I think that was the way you described him."

"You know it was," she muttered resentfully. "I didn't realize anyone had heard what we had to say."

"It wasn't intentional." He pushed back a dark swathe of hair with impatient fingers, as if its thick vitality irritated him. "But just because you consider him to be all of those things doesn't mean he's incapable of appreciating a beautiful woman."

Stacy blushed, although the words were in no way presented as a compliment, but more as a statement of facts. She knew she was attractive—in her job she had to be aware of her own potential—but this man had made it almost seem a crime for her slender figure, waist-length red hair, sparkling green eyes, small uptilted nose and wide smiling mouth to be in the least beautiful.

Her eyes flashed angrily, her lashes naturally sooty and long. "Well, as he's never seen me he won't know what he's missing," she snapped. Really, this man was very arrogant!

Even his stance was arrogant, his legs slightly apart, challenge in every muscle and sinew. "But he has seen you, several times in fact," he told her calmly.

She frowned. "I'm sure I would have remembered it."

"Really?" he asked mockingly. "Do you remember every short, fat, balding man that makes your acquaintance."

She flushed angrily. "You overheard a purely private conversation, and it's very rude of you to keep reminding me of it."

"I stand rebuked," he taunted.

"You're damned arrogant!" she said tautly.

He gave a deep husky laugh, an attractive sound that made her nerve endings tingle. His teeth were firm and white against the dark tan of his skin, and he looked younger when he laughed, although she would say he was in his late thirties. The fine lines at the corner of his eyes and mouth were an indication of the licentious life he had led the last thirty-seven, thirty-eight years.

"So I've been told," he acknowledged without shame.

"I'm sure I would have remembered if I had met Mr. Weston. Besides, he only arrived today, and I've only just got back to the hotel."

He still looked amused. "I didn't say you had met him, I said he had seen you—on film. Your screen test, actually. There were over a hundred applicants for that part when they narrowed the field down, and he wanted to choose the girl for that part himself. He chose you."

"I didn't realize."

"Although only a small part he considered that role important—the girl Jason eventually marries."

She looked surprised. "You seem to know a lot about it."

"I would hardly be a good employee if I didn't take an interest in my employer's work."

"What exactly do you do?"

He shrugged his wide powerful shoulders. "This and that."

"I see."

"I doubt it," he mocked, not rising to her contempt. "But I really couldn't give a damn. So, the reason you've been fired?"

She gave a defiant flick of her head, her long red tresses flying back over her shoulder. "If you're that interested, ask the director."

"He's the one who dismissed you?"

She grinned, her good humor never down for long, as she remembered the interview she had just been through with Martin Payne. "You could say that," she agreed.

"Then I'll talk to him."

Stacy shrugged. "Please yourself. I have to go and change for dinner. Excuse me." She walked off before he could answer her.

"You didn't tell me your name," he called after her.

She hesitated with her key in the door to her room, turning to look at him as he stood several feet away from her. "My name? You seem to be the one with all the answers, so find out." She quickly opened the door, slamming it hurriedly behind her.

She leaned back against the door, smiling impishly at her roommate, who sat on one of the single beds yawning tiredly. As one of the unknowns in the film, Stacy didn't merit being given a room of her own. Luckily she liked Juliet Small, which was perhaps as well in the circumstances. Juliet had a slightly smaller part than Stacy, another love of the hero Jason, and so she supposed it was only natural for them to be put in the same room.

Juliet was slightly older than her, twenty-five to her nineteen, with bubbly black curls and an impish face. She stood up now, stretching her aching limbs. "God, I'm tired," she groaned. "I had to go through that scene in the hayloft with Paul Forbes so many times today that I feel positively unclean."

Stacy grimaced, beginning to unpeel the figure-hugging dress from her own tired limbs. "I'm not surprised, having to let him paw you all over like that."

Juliet grinned. "Oh, I didn't mind that. It was all that hay—I have an allergy to it."

"And I have an allergy to Paul Forbes." She stepped out of the dress completely, clothed now in only a pair of minute briefs. "Thank God I don't have to let him touch me," she shuddered at the thought, going through to the adjoining bathroom to run the water for her shower.

Juliet followed her. "But you have the rape scene," she shouted above the roar of the water. "And you can bet your life on it that Paul Forbes will want that to be very explicit."

"Then he can damn well want," Stacy said sharply. "Even if I were staying I wouldn't allow him to do more than give a token show of rape."

"Yes, but you know him, he—*If* you were staying?"

"I'll be leaving tomorrow, Juliet," she said with a sigh, explaining her reasons. "I'm afraid he has picked on the wrong girl for his next affair," she added. "He just sickens me."

Juliet nodded. "At forty-three I think he's rather disgusting to want someone of nineteen." She patted her own glowing curls. "I'm much more his age," she teased.

"Juliet!" She couldn't help laughing. "You don't really like *him*?"

"Well .... Let's just say that it wasn't all acting today. I could have quite enjoyed it if it hadn't been for that hay."

Stacy stepped under the water, soaping her body. "Shame!" she taunted lightly. "Rather you than me."

She rinsed herself before turning off the shower and step-ping out into the towel Juliet held out to her. "Now I've just been accosted by what I would call a real man—and I do mean *real*."

"Well, don't keep him all to yourself. Who was he? *Where* is he?"

Stacy laughed softly. "By this time he should be upstairs with his employer, Jake Weston."

"So, what's he like?"

"Tall, dark, handsome, very muscular, arrogant, experi-enced—very experienced, I would say."

"He sounds dreamy."

"Oh, he is." In fact Stacy was surprised at the impression the man had made on her. She could still remember the cynical twist to that firm mouth and the taunting mockery of his deep blue eyes. "A little overpowering, but definitely dreamy."

"What's his name?" Juliet sat back on the bed, her chin resting on her denim-clad knees.

That brought Stacy up with a start. "Do you know, I have no idea. He didn't say and I didn't think to ask." Although after the way she had refused to tell him her name, she doubted he would be any more forthcoming.

"Bowled over by his charm?"

She smiled, taking her gown for the evening off the rack in the wardrobe. "Not exactly. I didn't say he was charm-ing."

"Oh, I see. So he doesn't have charm to go with all these other attributes?"

"I think he could have, I just didn't see any evidence of it. Are you going to the party tonight? I could show him to you then; he's bound to be there."

"Oh, I'm going. With him *and* Paul Forbes in atten-dance, I wouldn't miss it for anything."

Stacy laughed. "No one seems at all interested in meeting the famous author."

"Oh, I want to meet him, too. He's such a mystery man that I just have to see what he looks like. He's never photographed, you know, not even on the back of his books. He guards his privacy with fanatic intensity."

Stacy nodded. "I think the man I met just now may have been a sort of bodyguard. He certainly had the physique for it. But from what I can gather, Mr. Weston isn't worth photographing. I suggested to this other fellow that he was short, fat and bald, and he didn't deny it."

"Not very loyal of him."

"How can he deny it if it's the truth?"

"Mm," Juliet reluctantly agreed. "And here I was hoping he guarded his privacy because he's so good-looking."

"Hard luck," Stacy said unsympathetically. "You had better get ready; we'll have to go down to dinner soon."

She dressed while Juliet went into the bathroom. Her white gown was square necked, with narrow shoulder straps and a thick band of embroidered flowers at the waist before it flared out in four layers of pleated chiffon to just below her knee. It was a beautiful gown and made her hair appear redder than usual. It had been an expensive gown, too, and in the light of today's events she wished she had saved the money to help her through what could be weeks of being out of work.

She applied a light makeup, the natural brightness of her green eyes and her thick sooty lashes needing no adornment. She felt very satisfied with the result by the time she at last surveyed herself in the full-length mirror. As a final gesture she pinned the white gauzy rose she had bought to go with the gown over her left ear in the waving thickness of her hair. It gave her a Gypsy look and she felt pleased with her appearance.

Juliet seconded her opinion when she came out of the bathroom a few minutes later, her own gown a royal-blue silk that clung to her curves and gave a black sheen to her hair.

They made a lovely contrast when they entered the dining room together, and several male heads turned to look in their direction. They joined Matthew and his roommate, Daniel, at their table. Stacy had a hurried look around the large room once they had ordered their meal, just to see if her arrogant stranger was present.

He wasn't, although she supposed that if his employer had an aversion to meeting people he would probably be eating with him upstairs in his suite. She couldn't help but feel slightly disappointed, although he should be at the party being held in one of the private lounges. She found herself looking forward to seeing him again, even though he had been so disagreeable.

Matthew snapped his fingers in front of her eyes. "Hey, come back to us, dreamboat," he teased. "Surely our company isn't that boring?"

She turned to give him a dazzling smile. "You aren't boring at all. I was just deep in thought."

"I'm not needed tomorrow—would you like me to give you a lift up to London?"

"I wouldn't want to put you to all that trouble," she refused. "I can easily get a train."

"Certainly not. I'll take you."

"Well, if you're sure...."

"I'm sure," he said firmly.

She smiled again, her green eyes glowing. "In that case, I accept. I didn't particularly relish the idea of carrying a couple of suitcases to and from the station."

"You never know," put in Daniel. "You may even get an invite to stay the night."

Matthew grinned. "You don't know Stacy very well if you think that. All that fiery hair and the invitation in her eyes could mean she has a passionate nature—but I've never been allowed to find out. Stacy is waiting for someone to marry her before she makes that kind of commitment."

Daniel leaned forward to hold her hand. "Will you marry me?" he asked, his eyes full of merriment.

She laughed at his teasing. "I would actually want the wedding ring on my finger before I allowed you to do more than hold my hand," she warned.

He moved away in mock horror. "In that case... will *you* marry me, Juliet?"

"The same conditions apply, I'm afraid."

Daniel sat back with a sigh. "I wish someone would tell me where all these girls that belong to the permissive society are, because I've certainly never met any of them."

They all laughed together at his woebegone expression, quietening down as their meal arrived. They were a boisterous lot working on this film and Stacy felt sure the staff of this hotel was accustomed to a much more sober clientele, although they seemed to be coping with them quite well.

It was almost nine o'clock by the time they left the dining room, the meal superb as usual. Paul Forbes had passed their table on his way out, giving Stacy a cold look that left her in no doubt as to his feelings toward her now. She had shrugged this off resignedly—after tomorrow she wouldn't have to worry about him anymore.

She felt a certain amount of regret about leaving, not about her decision concerning Paul Forbes's advances, but because she had enjoyed working with the majority of the people here.

There were quite a lot of people already in the lounge when they got there, each of them grabbing a glass of cham-

pagne as a waiter hurried past them. There was soft background music drifting out from the strategically placed
speakers, although the babble of conversation drowned a
lot of this out.

Matthew stayed at her side, grinning down at her. "I
can't see our famous author yet."

Neither could she, but she could see her handsome
stranger standing at the other side of the room with Martin
Payne. He looked devastatingly attractive in a wine-colored
velvet jacket that fitted tautly across his wide, powerful
shoulders, a snowy white shirt with a ruffled front and black
trousers that molded to his firm muscular thighs. He stood
head and shoulders above any other man in the room and
was easily the most handsome man here.

He moved slightly and for the first time Stacy saw the
man standing at his side. She knew straight away that this
must be Jake Weston; he fitted her description perfectly,
even to the bald head.

She turned with a triumphant smile. "I wish I'd made a
bet over Mr. Weston," she said to Matthew.

"Mm?" He followed her line of vision. "It looks as if
you would have won."

The handsome stranger turned to look at them as if
aware of their scrutiny, nodding distantly as he recognized
Stacy. She nodded back before he turned away again, feeling strangely breathless at the brooding expression in his
eyes.

Matthew looked at her with raised eyebrows. "Who was
that?"

She took a sip of her drink, giving him a composed look.
"I have no idea."

He gave a splutter of laughter. "No idea when he looks at
you like that?" He shook his head. "The man was mentally
undressing you."

She colored delicately. "Can I help that?"

"No, I suppose not, not the way you look tonight. Did I tell you how beautiful you look?"

"No."

"Well, you do. Payne's a fool to drop you from this film. You're going to be a really big name one day." He looked up as a shadow fell across them in the dimmed room.

Stacy looked up, too, straight into those compelling blue eyes set in the deeply tanned face. "Hello," she said huskily, unable to think of anything more intelligent to say.

He nodded. "Good evening," he drawled. "I have something I would like to talk to you about, Miss Adams."

Matthew took the hint. "I'll just go and get another drink from the bar," he said quietly. "Can I get you anything, Stacy?"

"Er, no, no, thank you." She felt mesmerized by this tall arrogant stranger, unable to look away from his compelling features.

"Okay, I'll see you later, then." Matthew nodded to the other man before leaving.

"You found out my name." She said the first thing that came into her head.

He nodded, a mocking smile lifting the corners of his mouth. "Stacy Adams," he drawled slowly. "Very professional."

She flushed at his intended mockery. "There's nothing professional about it; it happens to be my name," she snapped. "At least, the name I was given at the orphanage," she added resentfully.

He looked unperturbed. "How long were you in the orphanage?"

"All my life, until I was sixteen."

"Poor kid," he said softly.

Her eyes flashed angrily. "I had quite a happy childhood as childhoods go. I certainly don't need your sympathy."

"You aren't getting it," he retorted harshly. "I came over here to tell you that you've been reinstated. You still have the part of Kate."

CHAPTER TWO

SHE SHOOK HER HEAD disbelievingly. "I don't understand. Mr. Payne sacked me."

"And now he's changed his mind."

Stacy gave him a sharp look. "This is your doing, isn't it? You got him to change his mind."

He gave a soft laugh. "How could I get him to do that? I don't have that sort of influence."

"You spoke to Mr. Weston, then."

"And if I did?" He watched her through narrowed eyes. "You're making it sound as if you would rather be out of a job."

"No, I—But what about Paul Forbes? He isn't going to like it."

"No one's asking him to. Just leave Forbes to me."

"But I—"

"Forget about him, Stacy," he ordered abruptly. "Just concentrate on playing Kate."

"You know my name, but I don't know yours," she said almost shyly.

"It's Jake."

She frowned. "Don't you find that rather confusing?"

"Not at all. Does my name bother you, because if it does, you could always change it. What would you like my name to be?"

Stacy gave a nervous laugh. "Stop teasing me."

"So who's teasing? What's in a name, anyway? My

mother named me and you were given yours by some stranger at the orphanage, but who's to say either of us has the right name for us. You can have whatever name you choose. Do you like the name Stacy?"

"Yes, yes, I do."

"So do I." He nodded agreement. "But I'm not that worried whether I'm called Jake or Harry, or any other name for that matter. You choose."

She laughed shakily. "You're mad. There's nothing wrong with your name; I was just surprised that it was the same as your employer's."

He shrugged. "That's something that can't be helped. I'm sure there must be thousands of Jakes in the world. I was bound to meet a few of them."

"Okay, okay," she laughed, feeling as if they were going around and around in circles. "I give in . . . Jake."

The intimacy of his gaze deepened. "I wish all my women conceded defeat that easily," he said softly, almost caressingly.

"I'm not conceding defeat, and I'm certainly not one of your women!" she snapped.

"How old are you, Stacy?"

"What does that have to do with anything?"

"Just answer the question."

"I'm nineteen," she told him resentfully.

"And I'm exactly twice that," he mused. "And yet I want you to know that I find you very attractive, very desirable."

"You—" she gulped. "You do?"

"I do," he confirmed. "Has anyone told you that you look beautiful tonight?"

She was becoming increasingly embarrassed, finding his sudden compliments a little *too* sudden. "It has been mentioned." She was deliberately blasé about it.

"By Matthew Day?" he probed harshly.

"How did you—"

"I'm paid to know things," he interrupted. "Have you been dating him long?"

"Didn't your informant tell you that?" she inquired sweetly.

"I didn't ask them, I'm asking you."

"I've known Matthew for three years."

"That doesn't exactly answer my question," he said dryly.

"No," she agreed.

"By that I take it you aren't going to answer it."

"You take it right." She imitated his American drawl. "I don't consider it any of your business."

"Not even if I wanted to date you myself?"

"And do you?" she challenged.

He let his gaze wander slowly over her body. "Oh, yes, I think so."

Stacy blushed scarlet. She had told Juliet that she thought he could have charm, but nothing had prepared her for this blatant approach. "I'm very flattered, Jake, but I—"

"Don't refuse me yet," he cut in. "Leave it until the end of the evening and see how you feel about me then."

"That almost sounds like a warning of intent."

He raised one dark eyebrow. "Only almost?"

She moved nervously, feeling way out of her depth with this man. "I, er, I think I should go and find Matthew."

He took the empty glass out of her hand, those long tapered fingers brushing gently against her skin. "No need, I'll go and get you another drink."

"That wasn't the reason I wanted him."

"Wait here," Jake ordered. "I won't be long."

She watched him stride away, aware of a feeling of pride as the female heads turned to watch his progress over to the bar. He was definitely a handsome specimen, and for some unexplainable reason he seemed to have chosen to spend the rest of the evening with her. She should feel flattered, but fear was one of her predominant emotions, fear of the mesmerizing effect he had on her.

She looked up warily as Martin Payne came toward her, the jovial smile on his face nothing like his anger with her earlier today. "Ah, Miss Adams." He beamed. "I trust Jake has told you that our little misunderstanding is to be forgotten?"

"He did mention it."

"Such a silly misunderstanding," he continued. "You only had to tell me that you had already agreed to come to the party with Jake and all of that unpleasantness could have been avoided."

So that's how he had done it! "I don't think—"

"I felt slightly ridiculous when he explained the circumstances behind your refusal." He smiled as he realized he was allowing anger to enter his voice. "I hope you will be able to forget any unpleasantness that may have occurred between us. It was all a complete mistake."

"Yes," she agreed uncertainly, not at all sure of his sudden change of mood. And she was a little curious as to why Jake had told this man she was spending the evening with him, although she realized this was probably what had saved her job. Martin Payne wouldn't want to antagonize anyone close to Jake Weston.

"Of course, I don't know how you managed it," he added curtly, obviously not completely cowed.

Stacy stiffened. "Don't you?" she queried softly, looking past him to the tall imposing figure of Jake as he had made his way back to her side, a drink in each hand.

Martin Payne flushed as he followed her line of vision. "Mm, well, perhaps I do," he muttered. "But for your sake I hope you never anger him as you did me this afternoon.

He would make a much more formidable adversary than I ever would."

She already knew that! She smiled at the director. "I don't envisage anything like that happening."

"I wouldn't count on it. People like Jake can be very temperamental."

Jake arrived at her side, smiling down at her as he handed her her drink, a completely charming smile directed at her, only at her. And it had the desired effect—she felt as if her legs were turning to jelly and there was a strange butterfly sensation in the pit of her stomach.

He turned to look at the director, his smile fading. "Martin," he nodded curtly.

"I, er, I just came over to tell Miss Adams that it will no longer be necessary for her to leave tomorrow." Martin Payne was obviously just as overwhelmed by this man as she was. "And to apologize for the misunderstanding."

Jake nodded. "I had already told her, but I'm sure she appreciated your telling her personally." Stacy felt herself stiffen as he put an arm possessively about her waist. "Stacy was rather upset about it all," he added.

"I'm sure she was." The older man looked uncomfortable. "Would you like me to introduce you to some of the other people here, now?"

"I don't think so," Jake refused, his hand on her waist seeming to burn where it touched. "Stacy and I can manage just fine on our own."

"But, Jake, this is all—"

"I said we can manage," Jake cut in. "Stacy can introduce me to anyone I care to meet, can't you, honey?"

"Er,—yes, yes, I suppose so."

The director shrugged. "Okay, then." He accepted defeat in the face of such obstinacy. "But I think Paul would like to meet you again."

"I'm sure he would," Jake snapped, his mouth a thin straight line. "But that's the one person I don't think Stacy would like to introduce me to. And I certainly don't appreciate men of his type trying to force young girls into going out with him."

"I'll, er, I'll see you later, then."

Jake was looking down at Stacy. "Perhaps, Martin. Perhaps."

It was a disgruntled Martin Payne who finally left them, and Stacy wondered at Jake for daring to talk to him in that way. After all, he was one of the leading directors in the world, and Jake had more or less dismissed him.

She looked up at Jake, moving out of the hold he had about her waist. "That isn't going to make you very popular," she warned.

He looked unperturbed. "I'm not out to win any popularity contests."

"Perhaps that's as well." She sipped her drink. "Mm, my favorite drink, martini and lemonade. Did your informant tell you that, too?"

He grinned at her, his eyes deeply blue. "I don't have an informant. I guessed about your drink, and as for the other, well, I just asked Payne why he had dismissed you."

She looked surprised. "And he told you about Paul Forbes?"

"Not exactly."

"But you worked it out," she said knowingly.

"Knowing Paul as I do, yes."

Her eyes widened. "You know him?" she asked almost accusingly.

"Slightly."

Her mouth compressed. "I see."

"I don't think you do. Let's sit down and we'll talk about it." Without waiting for her answer, he led her over to a secluded table, in the dimmer lighting, well away from everyone else. He pulled out a chair for her to sit down and then sat at her side, his arm resting along the back of her chair.

Stacy was very aware of the warmth of his arm against her bare skin, the velvet material of his jacket pleasurably caressing her back. She sat forward to avoid the intimacy of that touch. "You were saying you know Paul Forbes." She couldn't even bring herself to look at him, she was so aware of him.

Why should he be interested in her, anyway? There were plenty of much more beautiful women here tonight who would be only too pleased to be with such a distinguished, attractive man. And yet he had chosen her.

He gently pushed her back in the seat, leaning forward himself to prevent her moving again. Now Stacy felt hemmed in by him, unable to look anywhere else but at his dark compelling face. The expression in his eyes was not one she cared to analyze.

"I did say I know Paul, but not in the way you mean. I know him slightly, but I know *of* him better. His reputation for liking young girls is well known. Although in your case I can't exactly blame him."

"Well, I can," she said angrily. "He's disgusting."

"I agree," he drawled. "But then you shouldn't be so damned beautiful."

She blushed fiery red. "He didn't want me because of my looks, he wanted me because I don't want him."

Jake sat back, crossing one leather-clad foot over the other. "Feminine logic?"

"If you like," she said stiffly. "If I showed an interest in him he wouldn't want me. I have a friend who thinks he's fantastic, but adoration isn't what he wants. Oh, no, Paul Forbes likes his women unwilling."

"Really?" He sounded amused.

"Yes, *really*!" she snapped. "And it isn't in the least funny!"

"I couldn't agree more," he said grimly.

"You...you couldn't?"

"I wouldn't like to think that you could be attracted to someone like him."

Stacy looked puzzled. "He's a very attractive man, a lot of women would feel honored to go out with him. He's tall, very good-looking, has lovely styled blond hair, and the most twinkling blue eyes I've ever seen. He's very young looking for his age, too."

"Does that mean you find him attractive?" he asked harshly.

She couldn't repress her shudder of disgust. "No."

"Good. Because besides those obvious attributes he's nothing but a bastard. If I thought you could go out with him I wouldn't be sitting here."

"No one's asking you to stay," she said in a stilted voice. "You seem to have invited yourself to sit with me."

He restrained her from moving by the tight hold he had of her wrist. "Stay here, Stacy. Don't be so sensitive. It's just that I consider Paul Forbes to be the lowest form of life, a man who trades on his wealth and fame."

"Any man in his position would do the same."

"Jake Weston hasn't."

Stacy looked with amusement at the author as he chatted amiably with a group of people on the other side of the room. She turned back to her companion, her green eyes twinkling merrily. "I hope you'll excuse my saying so, but he doesn't really have a lot going for him."

"No, I don't suppose he does. Tell me about yourself, Stacy," he commanded abruptly.

"Have you finished questioning me about Paul Forbes?" she asked tartly.

Jake sat forward, running a caressing finger down her cheek. "I was just curious as to why you refused his invitation."

"And now you're satisfied?"

His blue eyes mocked her. "Hardly. But that can come later when you know me a little better."

"You mean—" She broke off in confusion.

"I mean exactly what you think I mean. But don't worry, I'll give you time to get to know me first."

She gave an incredulous laugh. "Are you honestly trying to tell me—"

"I believe in being honest about these things," he interrupted. "I want to go to bed with you; I want to put my brand of possession on you as soon as possible, so there's no point in trying to hide it. I told you earlier that I find you desirable."

"Yes, but—"

"I know, I know, you take things a little slower over here. I've lived in the States so long I've forgotten I'm supposed to be one of the reserved English."

Stacy gave him a curious look. "You aren't American?"

"As good as; I left England when I was five years old. I was born not far from here. I guess I'll have to try and get a little of this reserve you all seem to have. But like I said, I'm not going to rush you into anything. If you find you don't feel the same way about me after a couple of dates then we'll forget the whole thing. I *don't* like my women unwilling."

She swallowed hard, aware of the sensuous allure of his body as he sat beside her. Any woman could be seduced by such virility as he displayed, and she wasn't immune to him—far from it. She could easily find herself falling for him. "And I don't go in for casual affairs," she told him softly.

He looked at her with brooding eyes, their color very

blue. "I didn't say there was going to be anything casual about it."

"And I don't intend to be your bed companion for the short time you'll be in this country, either."

"What makes you think I'm only going to be here a short time?"

She shrugged. "As far as I know Mr. Weston is only here for the last couple of weeks of filming. As his employee you'll leave when he does."

"Then I'll just have to make sure he enjoys his stay enough to want to stay longer."

"I wouldn't bother on my account." She put her empty glass down on the table. "I think I should go and find Matthew."

His eyes narrowed. "You never did tell me how friendly you are with him."

"Very friendly." She deliberately gave the wrong impression of that friendship.

Those long fingers clamped about her wrist once again. "Is that the truth, Stacy?"

She faced him defiantly. "Why should I lie?"

"Fear. Nervousness. There could be any number of reasons."

It was both of those, and a lot more. The trouble with this man was that he was too attractive for any woman to resist for long. Not that it made him conceited—he had merely seen something he wanted and wasn't afraid to say so. But his age and experience made her nervous, gave her the feeling that this was a battle she was going to lose, which was why she had to stop it now.

"Matthew and I are very good friends. We even lived together for a time." Which they had, on a purely platonic basis. Matthew had been thrown out of his apartment, so she had let him sleep on her sofa for a while.

"But not now?" Jake persisted.

"Not now."

The tension seemed to leave his body. "Then it couldn't have worked out between the two of you, which means there's nothing between you now. I'm not asking for virginity from you, Stacy."

"I don't think you have the right to ask anything of me." She gave him a searching look. "I hardly know you, but I can tell you're no novice when it comes to making love."

"At thirty-eight, no."

"Not even at my age," she rebuked.

"Probably not," he acknowledged mildly.

"I would say definitely not."

He laughed softly. "I think you're right." He stood up. "Let's go for a walk in the garden."

She looked up at him, wrenching her eyes away from his muscular thighs only inches in front of her. "It's after ten o'clock at night; it's dark out there."

He pulled her effortlessly to her feet, retaining a hold of one of her hands as she would have pulled away. "The garden is illuminated at night," he said tolerantly.

"Yes, but I—"

"Come on, Stacy. It's too noisy in here; we can't talk properly."

"I think we've talked enough for one day."

"About certain things, perhaps, but I have other things to say to you." His voice lowered. "Things I would rather say when we're completely alone."

That's what she was afraid of! "No, I don't think—"

"I'm not asking you to think. Don't be such a baby, Stacy. Is there no adventure in your soul, no craving for danger?"

Not when she had a good chance of losing to him! "No," she said huskily.

"I don't believe you."

He pulled her along behind him and Stacy had no choice but to follow him. She was conscious of many people curiously watching their exit and this didn't improve her mood.

She pulled away from him once they were outside, glaring at him resentfully, her color heightened. "It's cold out here," she lied. "I want to go back inside."

His answer was to put an arm about her shoulders and pull her against the side of his firm muscular body. "It isn't cold, Stacy," he contradicted. 'But if you are, just stay close to me. I'll keep you warm."

"Perhaps that's what I'm afraid of."

"That's what I thought." He turned to face her, his arms about her waist as he molded her thighs to his. "I can't do much to you in a garden, now can I?"

She gulped. "I suppose not."

"Besides, I like the comfort of a bed when I make those sort of advances. I've gone past the impetuous youth bit where I can make love anywhere. Also, I want things to be right between us the first time."

She gulped again. This man was unlike anyone else she had ever known, *said* things no one else would dare to say on such short acquaintance. "The—" she licked her dry lips "—the first time?"

"The first time we make love," he told her calmly.

She gave a short breathless laugh. "I can't decide whether you're conceited *or* I've just gone mad," she said dazedly.

"Neither of those things," Jake murmured huskily, his eyes never leaving her parted lips. "Your mouth was made for kissing. I've wanted to kiss you ever since I saw you in the elevator this evening."

"But you . . . you were so distant."

His dark eyebrows rose. "I could hardly make love to you

in an elevator, and I don't think you would have let me on such short acquaintance. Besides, I knew you were going to be here this evening. It was the only thing that persuaded me to be here at all."

All the time they were talking she was aware of the hardness of his body curved into her own, her hands crushed against his chest. "But surely you had to be here to protect your employer?"

"Does it look as if I'm doing much protecting?"

"No," she admitted.

"That's because I'm not. I abhor parties and I dislike crowds. I'm only here to see you."

"You flatter me."

"Maybe, but I don't usually put myself out for other people."

He was very arrogant, considering he was only a lowly employee like herself. "You're very lucky if you don't have to. Some of us aren't so lucky."

"You don't seem to have made any concessions in your argument with Payne this afternoon," he taunted.

She blushed. "That was different."

"Not at all. You make your own set of rules and you have to live by them." His hold about her waist tightened. "And I'm very glad you kept to yours today. It could have caused quite a scene if I'd had to fight Forbes to get you."

Her eyes widened. "You would have done that?"

"Oh, yes, Stacy, I would have done that."

"You make it very hard for a girl to refuse you."

His head bent slightly, his face only inches away from her own. "That's because I don't intend to have you refuse me. I'm patient; I can wait for the right moment."

"And if there isn't one?" she murmured.

"Than I'll make one."

His dark head lowered slowly and his lips took possession

of hers in a kiss of languorous passion, a deliberate on-slaught to break down any barriers she might have against him. He needn't have worried—his charm had seduced her into submission long ago.

But this was wrong! She had known this man only a mat-ter of hours. And yet she couldn't hold back her response, couldn't deny the effect he was having on her, his mouth making slow leisurely love to her, his hands gently caress-ing her back.

Finally she pulled away from him, her head dizzy with the emotions he had aroused in her, emotions that had lain dormant until his mouth had touched hers. This couldn't be happening to her—it must be his experience that was mak-ing her melt against him like this—people didn't fall in love so easily.

She licked her lips, tasting the whiskey Jake had been drinking earlier, her whole body shaking. "I—" She cursed herself for letting her voice shake like this. "I want to go back inside," she said more strongly.

"Why?" he asked huskily, not releasing his hold on her.

"I think you know why."

"Because I kissed you?"

And because of her reaction to that kiss! "Well, I—Yes! I hardly know you," she added, as if that explained every-thing.

"Mm, perhaps you're right." He moved away from her. "My mother always told me you should never kiss a girl on your first date." He smiled. "I never did listen to my mother."

Stacy smoothed down her gown. "Then perhaps you should have."

"Perhaps." But he didn't sound as if he should. "I'll take you back to the party now."

"I think I would rather go to my room."

"So would I," he agreed throatily.

"Alone," she said sharply.

"But of course. I promise to leave you at your door."

"I can find my own way," she replied.

He took hold of her elbow. "I'm sure you can, but I've always believed in seeing a lady to her home, and as this place is temporarily your home...."

"Oh, all right," she accepted reluctantly.

Jake grinned down at her as they walked back to the entrance. "I wish I could have seen your argument with Payne. I bet it was something to watch."

Stacy gave a wan smile. "He didn't seem to think so."

"So he told me. I believe you implied he was past it."

She blushed painfully as she remembered the rude things she had said to the director.

"Something about us being past the age of the studio couch," he added teasingly.

"Oh, oh, yes," she blushed even more. "I...I lost my temper."

He laughed softly. "So I gathered." He picked up a strand of her glorious red hair. "So this hair really does denote the fiery nature reputed to go with it."

"In my case, yes," she admitted almost guiltily.

Jake tilted her chin. "I like the temper. It adds to your attraction."

"It does?"

"I like a woman who can stand up for herself."

"Oh."

"You aren't sure that's a good thing, are you?"

"No," she answered truthfully. She held back as he opened the door for her. "Could we go in another way?"

"Why?" he looked at her suspiciously.

"Well, because I...I...."

His teeth gleamed whitely in the darkness. "Your lipstick

isn't smudged, if that's what you're worried about." He gently touched her lips as if to emphasize the point.

Her breath caught in her throat. "It isn't that."

"Then what is it?" His hand dropped away from her mouth.

She gave an impatient sigh. "I don't want to simply walk through the room and then go upstairs together. I know exactly what conclusion the people in there would come to."

"You do?"

"Yes," she snapped. "And don't pretend that you don't, too."

He shut the door with a shrug. "Okay, we'll sneak in the back way."

"I didn't mean—"

"Grow up, Stacy!" He was angry now. "Do you think the fact that we just disappear is going to give them any less food for thought? I would have thought it would have given them even more to get their teeth into."

"Damn you!" Her eyes blazed angrily. "Damn you, damn you!" She flung open the door, marching into the room, uncaring about whether or not he followed her in.

She walked gracefully across the room with unhurried steps, looking neither left nor right, a defiant look to her mouth and an angry glitter to her eyes. As she reached the reception area the anger started to leave her tensed body. After all, she shouldn't let a comparative stranger annoy her like this.

It wasn't until she put her hand out to press the elevator button and a long tanned muscular hand beat her to it that she realized Jake was standing beside her. She stubbornly refused to look at him although all her senses told her it was him, from the pleasant aroma of his after-shave to the much more potent male smell that belonged exclusively to him. He had done nothing but anger or excite her since the moment they had met, and she would no longer give him that satisfaction.

Once inside the elevator she still kept her eyes averted, although it was becoming increasingly difficult to do so. Finally she just had to look at him, the silence between them oppressive, only to find his caressing gaze fixed on her face.

"Oh!" she gasped, looking hurriedly away again.

He moved to stand in front of her, a hand on the wall on either side of her head, his body only just separate from her own. He looked at her beneath lowered lids. "I told you I like the temper. You won't get rid of me that way."

"I wasn't trying—"

"Oh, yes, you were, and we both know why. If what I said earlier bothers you that much just forget I said it."

"It isn't the sort of thing you can forget. It isn't every day a man tells me he would like to go to bed with me."

"Maybe other men don't tell you, but they think it." He lifted her chin so that she had no choice but to look at him. "Is it because I'm so much older than you that you find the prospect so daunting? Or is it that you think I only want you for one night and then I'll pass on to another conquest?"

"Both of those things," she croaked. And more, much more!

"I can't refute the latter; I have no idea how a relationship between us would turn out, and I've never considered my age a barrier before. Or is it the experience that goes with the age that bothers you; the other women I've known and left?"

"Yes! And...and we've known each other such a short time."

Suddenly he had moved away and was standing on the other side of the elevator, extracting a long thin cheroot from a gold case before lighting it. "I wouldn't insult you by asking you to go to bed with me now. All the best things in life are worth waiting for... and you're one of them. It will happen in your time, not mine. Will you go swimming with me tomorrow morning?"

She should be perfectly safe with him in the hotel swimming pool; there were always a lot of people there. "What time?"

"Ten o'clock?"

She pressed the button to open the elevator doors. "Fine. I'll meet you downstairs in the reception area."

Jake held the doors open so that the elevator wouldn't move. "Off you go to your room, I won't go any farther and frighten you any more. Ten o'clock downstairs," he reminded as she hurried to her room.

As she let herself in with her key she had a last impression of him leaning against one of the elevator doors, watching her progress with dark brooding eyes.

She heaved a sigh of relief as she leaned back against the door. These sort of things didn't happen in real life—being pursued by tall, dark, handsome men with a stated intent on her virtue. But it *was* happening to her.

She was in bed pretending to be asleep when Juliet came up to bed. She had no wish to answer questions about Jake, especially questions she had no answer to. It was for this reason that she also pretended to be asleep the next morning as Juliet got ready to go down to breakfast. Once her friend had left she got up and ordered herself some coffee. She didn't intend seeing anyone who could ask embarrassing questions.

Jake was already waiting for her when she arrived downstairs at ten past ten, looking at her impatiently as she moved to the desk to leave a message for Matthew, telling him she wouldn't be needing transport into London after all.

"Good morning," Jake greeted softly. He was dressed in cream slacks and a matching short-sleeved shirt opened almost to his waist in the heat of the day. He looked very attractive; his skin appearing very dark against his cream clothing.

Stacy's eyes alighted on the picnic basket at his side. "What's in the basket?" she asked lightly.

"Our lunch."

"Lunch?" She frowned. "Surely we won't need that by the pool."

"We aren't going to the pool."

She looked up at him. "We...we aren't?"

He shook his head. "I've borrowed Payne's motor launch. We're going for a ride along the coast to find a secluded beach where I can seduce you in private."

CHAPTER THREE

So much for her being safe by the pool! "You didn't tell me that last night," she said resentfully. "I automatically took it you meant the pool."

"Does it matter?" He looked bored.

"Of course it matters," she said sharply.

"Why? Don't answer that, I think I can guess," his voice taunted. "You didn't expect to be alone with me today. Well, I'm not going to the pool so that all your friends can stare at us. I'm going out in the boat anyway; you please yourself if you come with me." He picked up the picnic basket. "But if you're too scared...." He shrugged, walking away.

Stacy caught up with him as he got in the low two-seater sports car parked outside, throwing the basket in the space at the back of the car. She got in beside him, her rolled up towel on her knee. "I'm not frightened of you." She glared at him furiously.

The car shot away with a roar, its driver turning to grin at her. "I knew you wouldn't be able to resist a challenge like that."

"Why you—"

"Fair's fair, Stacy. Last night you did agree to come with me."

"Yes, but— Oh, never mind," she said impatiently. "I bet you always win an argument."

"I try to. I was a very spoiled little boy."

"I can imagine," she retorted dryly.

"And I can imagine you as a very charming little girl."

"I wasn't." She laughed. "I was hateful. I was plump, had crooked teeth, and so many freckles it was hard to see where one ended and another began."

His gaze ran over her appreciatively in her lemon slacks and black top. "Looking at you now I would never believe it."

She blushed in confusion, realizing she had invited that compliment. "Oh, I would believe it, Jake, the hateful little girl underneath hasn't changed very much."

"Is that a warning?"

"If you like."

He laughed softly. "I like a challenge, too. No man has ever liked to win a woman too easily, just as he doesn't like to be the pursued instead of the pursuer."

"You think you're going to win with me?"

"I'm hoping so."

She gave him a pitying smile. "I wish you luck."

"I don't like the sound of that."

"You weren't meant to."

They were nearing the harbor now, the gleaming boats bobbing at their moorings. Jake parked the car, apparently knowing which boat belonged to Martin Payne. He carried the picnic basket over to a white gleaming boat, its sleek lines beautifully reflected in the still water.

"I didn't expect anything like this." She looked about the luxurious interior, coming back up on deck to sit on one of the plush leather seats.

Jake stowed the picnic basket down in the galley, unpacking a bottle of wine to put it in the small refrigerator provided. He came back up into the sunshine. "Just what did you expect?"

She shrugged. "I'm not really sure."

He grinned. "But certainly not this. I do know how to work it, you know."

Stacy looked at him, squinting in the bright sunshine. "I never for a moment doubted it."

He laughed softly. "Are you ready to leave?"

"Mm." She took a deep breath of the sea air. "I'm going to like this."

"I hope so." He quickly untied their moorings, guiding the boat out of the quiet harbor before increasing speed.

Stacy threw back her head, laughing as the wind blew through her hair. "Mm," she sighed, lying back on the seat that stretched across the back of the boat. "This is relaxing."

Jake turned briefly to look at her, his sunglasses shielding his eyes. "Did you bring any suntan oil with you? We're very lucky to be having such warm weather for this time of year, and although it may seem quite breezy out here the reflection of the sun on the water will burn your skin."

She sat up, delving into the recesses of her shoulder bag. She held up the tube of oil with a smile. "I thought I had some."

"Would you like me to rub it on for you?" he asked softly.

She blushed, imagining those long tapered fingers moving slowly over her body. "No, thank you," she said primly.

He grinned at her. "I somehow thought you would say that. Did you bring a bathing suit with you?"

"I have it on under my clothes." Thank goodness she had thought to take this precaution! She wouldn't have relished the idea of getting into her bikini with this man so near.

"Why don't you strip off and try to get a tan?"

"Er, no. I think I'll wait until we reach the cove."

He shrugged. "Please yourself. Take the helm for a while so I can get out of these hot clothes."

She stood up, looking at the controls uncertainly. "I'm not sure . . . ."

"Relax, honey. I'll be standing right behind you."

She sat down on the chair he had vacated for her, shivering slightly as his arms came on either side of her from behind to place her hands on the controls. His warm breath gently moved her hair against her cheek and she held her head rigid, conscious of just how close he was. She had only to turn her head slightly to the right and his mouth would be against her cheek.

But she wasn't going to turn her head! She had to be careful with this dangerous man, simply becuse he *was* dangerous. He ate up and spat out little girls like her almost every day of his life.

"Perhaps that's what I'm afraid of," she said huskily.

"You needn't be," he murmured close against her ear. "I won't ever do anything to you that you don't want me to."

"Then I wish you would move away from me." She gulped. "I don't like it," she lied.

The arms around her were instantly removed and he moved to stand beside her. He started unbuttoning the rest of his shirt, pulling it out of the waistband of his trousers. "Is that really true?" he asked softly.

She was aware of his bare torso as his hands lowered to the fastening of his trousers. She turned hurriedly away. "Yes," she snapped.

He threw his clothes down into the cabin and Stacy was tempted to turn to look at him. He was dressed only in navy-blue swimming trunks that molded to his lean hips. His body was tanned a deep brown all over—at least as far as she could see—a dark matt of hair covering his chest and finishing at his navel. His body was firm and muscular, and he was in much better condition physically than a lot of men half his age. He was just a damned attractive man—and each moment she found herself becoming more and more attracted to him.

He took over the steering of the boat. "Are you sure you don't want to take off those things?"

"Very sure." She studiously ignored him, rubbing oil into her bare arms.

"I'll see you when we get to the beach," he taunted. "I take it you are going to swim today?"

"I am."

"Then I'll just have to wait until then," he sighed.

"Shame," she teased, forgetting to be distant with him. "I can assure you that I don't have anything any other woman doesn't have. In fact, I'm a bit on the skinny side."

"Maybe I like my women skinny. The anticipation is certainly killing me."

"It's good for you." She grinned.

He snorted his disbelief. "You have to be kidding. How about that cove over there?"

Her eyes followed the direction he was pointing, seeing a sheltered beach completely cut off except by access from the sea, sheer rock face on either side of it. "It looks perfect," she admitted. And very secluded!

"Good." He swung the boat in the direction of the cove, slowing it down to gently maneuver it as far up the beach as he could. He managed to get it about six feet from the actual sand before the front of the boat hit bottom. "Well, this is as far as it goes." He turned to face her, hands on his hips. "I think you'll have to take off your slacks now, or you'll get them wet when we wade ashore."

"Okay." Her cheeks colored delicately. "You get the picnic basket and I'll get undressed."

"Can't I stay and watch?"

"No." She laughed.

"No?" he quirked an eyebrow.

"No." She laughed again.

"You can't hide from me forever, you know. Okay, okay, I'm going." He went down into the galley to get the food and wine.

Stacy took advantage of his absence to slip off her slacks and top, her light golden skin shown to advantage in the emerald-colored bikini. It was the briefest of bikinis, its only fastenings a knot between her breasts and one at each of her hips. She hadn't realized when she had chosen to wear it that they were to be alone like this, or she might not have been so daring in her choice.

Jake removed his sunglasses by the time he came back up on deck, his deep blue eyes slowly roving over her from head to toe. There could be no doubt that he found pleasure just in looking at her, and Stacy blushed as he made no effort to hide his arousal.

She turned away. "Don't look at me like that," she ordered huskily.

He broke his gaze as if in a daze. "Sorry," he said abruptly. "You're so damned beautiful," he murmured throatily.

"You'll make me conceited if you keep telling me such things." She blushed fiery red.

"Sorry," he said more briskly. "Come on, I'll help you over the side."

There was no avoiding his touch, and Stacy felt excitement course through her veins. As he slowly lowered her into the water his eyes held hers so that she couldn't look away, only the coolness of the water around her feet jolting her out of the spell he was casting over her. The water only came up to mid-calf, the sand smooth beneath her feet.

"Here." He handed her the chilled wine before climbing over the side himself, hoisting the picnic basket after him. He put this down on the sand beside her. "I'll just go and get some blankets to lie on and secure the boat. I wouldn't want the tide to come in before we'd realized it and the boat to drift away."

Stacy sat down on the sand, amazed at how warm it was here, the high rocks on either side of them stopping all the wind.

Jake dropped her sunglasses and handbag down on to the sand beside her before spreading out the blanket he had brought back. "I would put some more oil on that delicate skin of yours," he advised. "I'd hate you to burn up."

She did as he suggested, holding the bottle to him when she had finished. "Would you like some?"

"Not necessary. I have naturally dark skin and very rarely burn."

She watched as he picked up the bottle of wine, walking back to the water's edge to secure it between two rocks in the water. She frowned. "What did you do that for?"

"To keep it cool." He came back, sitting down at her side. "We aren't going to have lunch yet, and if I leave the wine out in the sun it will be a waste of time having put it in the refrigerator. The water will help keep it cool."

"You think of everything."

He gave a penetrating look. "I try to."

He certainly did. He had thought to bring the food, the wine, and he had borrowed that fantastic boat for the day. And all so that he could be alone with her. The thought terrified her.

She stood up hurriedly, activity helping to banish the intimacy of her imaginings. "Shall we swim?"

"Sure." He put out a hand for her to pull him to his feet and she had perforce to take it, the leverage pulling him dangerously close to her body. "Do you swim well, Stacy?"

She stepped back, pulling her hand free when he would have still held it. "Moderately so." She looked down at her feet in the silky sand.

"Mind the currents here, they can be treacherous," he warned.

She shivered as the cool water began to envelop her body. "I'm sure you'll be able to save me if I get into trouble," she said dryly. She felt sure he was as accomplished in swimming as he appeared to be at everything else.

"I hope so. But stay close to me—no going off on your own."

She immersed her shoulders in the water. "You're really serious about this, aren't you?"

"Very serious. People die along this part of the coast every year."

"Have you been here before?"

He swam off with long, easy strokes, turning to float on his back as she joined him. "I told you, I was born near here."

"Yes, but you...you speak as if you've been here recently."

"I have." He pushed the dark swathe of wet hair from his eyes. "The research for the book was done around here."

She nodded. "I suppose you stayed here with Mr. Weston?"

"Yes," he agreed tersely. He trod water. "You look like a mermaid lying there, your hair floating out behind you."

She turned over self-consciously. "Don't let me hold you back. I'm sure you're a much stronger swimmer than I am."

"Perhaps, but I didn't particularly come here to swim. I came here to be with you."

"Oh."

"Do I still frighten you, Stacy?"

He petrified her, but only because he was so attractive! "Yes," she admitted huskily.

He touched her wet cheek. "How can I stop you feeling this way?"

She swallowed hard. "I don't think you can." Unless he suddenly turned into a gargoil and lost all that sex appeal that simply oozed out of him. And that didn't seem very likely.

"Did my saying I desire you start this off?"

"Not particularly." She blushed. "Although it does come into it."

All the time he was moving closer to her, their bodies almost touching. "So that I don't shock you anymore I'm warning you now that I'm going to kiss you."

She had no time to protest before his mouth covered hers, both of them sinking below the water as the kiss intensified. Totally immersed in the water, the kiss seemed even more unreal, Jake's legs entwined with hers, their arms around each other.

The kiss seemed to last forever and ever, with Jake showing no signs of wanting to break it. Finally it was Stacy who had to wrench away, frantically kicking her feet to reach the surface. She came up spluttering, breathing deep gulps of air into her starved lungs.

Seconds later Jake appeared at her side, showing none of the near panic she had displayed, casually flicking his dark hair back from his face. He grinned at her. "I always wondered what that was like."

She gave him a scathing look. "You mean you've never done it before?"

"Have you?"

She frowned. "No."

"Neither have I."

"You surprise me," she said in a stilted voice, still shaking from the embrace.

"Do you like surprises?"

"Not particularly," she said slowly.

"Not at all?" he persisted.

"Only pleasant ones."

"I see."

"And I hate practical jokes," she added. "More often than not they turn out to be rather cruel on the poor victim."

"I'm sure they aren't meant to be."

"Possibly not, but they invariably are. I have a sense of humor like the next person, but I don't like cruelty." She gave a sudden laugh. "We've become very serious all of a sudden." She splashed water at him. "I thought we were here to enjoy ourselves."

"We are." He came toward her with strong strokes. "I think you deserve punishment for splashing me."

Stacy turned to swim away from the intimacy in his eyes. But she wasn't quick enough as he caught hold of her shoulders and pushed her under the water. She didn't manage to take in any air before she went under, clutching frantically at Jake for support. She only managed to make contact with his bathing trunks, and once she realized this she let go.

This time when she emerged above water her face was redder than her hair. She couldn't meet the mockery openly displayed in his eyes. "Sorry," she muttered.

"Don't be. That's the first time a woman has tried to rip my clothes off while I've been swimming."

"But not the first time a woman has tried to rip your clothes off," she taunted to cover her embarrassment.

"No," he laughingly agreed.

"Well, don't count that as a first," she was angered by his agreement. "It was purely accidental that I... that I—"

"Tried to take off my bathing trunks," he finished teasingly.

"I didn't!" she said crossly, her anger all the stronger because she could still remember the smoothness of his flesh beneath her hand. "At least not intentionally," she added resentfully.

Jake swam beside her. "I was only teasing you, honey."

"I know. But it is nearly lunchtime, and I didn't have any breakfast."

He shrugged. "I could use some food, too."

They dried themselves off with their towels before sitting down on the blanket. Stacy dealt with the food, glad to be able to do something to cover her embarrassment, and Jake uncorked the wine. There were cold meats and salad in the basket, besides cakes and fruit.

"Did you tell them at the hotel that it was just for two people?" She looked with despair at the cold beef and turkey, the mountain of salad stuff, and all the cakes and fresh fruit.

He paused in the opening of the wine. "Of course I did. Don't look so worried. I'm hungry, and you said you were, too."

"Yes, but—"

"You aren't one of those women who pick at their food because they think it looks polite, are you?" He frowned.

"Now when have I ever gone out of my way to be polite in front of you?"

He laughed softly. "Never. Perhaps that's why I like you so much." He gently touched one of her cheeks. "You're completely natural with me."

"Why shouldn't I be?"

His hand dropped away and he became engrossed in pouring out the wine. "No reason," he said abruptly. "Here." He handed her a brimming glass of the bubbly liquid.

She wrinkled her face as the bubbles tickled her nose. "Mm, it's lovely."

"Did you doubt it?" He looked offended.

"Not if you chose it, no."

His eyes narrowed as he looked out to sea, another boat slowly hovering on their shoreline. "Oh, hell," he muttered. "Don't put out any more food. If they stop here, we're moving on."

"But, Jake, we can't do that."

"Yes, we damn well can. I chose this beach because it's small and private. I don't want other people around. I want to be alone with you."

"Yes, but, well, wouldn't it look rather rude if we just packed up and left as soon as they arrived?" She frowned her consternation.

"I couldn't give a damn how it looks." He sighed his satisfaction. "It's all right, they seem to be moving on."

Stacy watched as the boat increased its speed around the headland and disappeared from their view. "Would you really have left if they had stopped here?" she asked curiously.

"Yes."

"Oh." She supposed she should really be flattered, but somehow it only made her more nervous. Why should Jake want such total privacy for them—unless he intended making love to her!

"Eat your food," he encouraged.

The food was all delicious, as she had known it would be. This man seemed to demand and receive the best, and somehow most of the food seemed to disappear.

The debris cleared away, they lay side by side on the blanket, a glass of wine beside them both. "You said you were born here," Stacy said sleepily. "Does that mean your mother and father are English?"

Jake turned on his side, leaning on his elbow to look down at her. "My mother is. My father was an American serviceman. They met before the war and were married here."

"Does your mother like living in America?" she asked, more for something to say than actual interest. Jake was lying much too close to her, his thigh touching her own, that she had to keep his attention on things other than herself.

"I've never asked her." His hand trailed down her bare arm. "But she rarely comes back here so I suppose she must."

"But you've never asked her," she said with amusement.

"Are you rebuking me?"

"Do you feel rebuked?" she teased.

"Yes."

"Then I suppose I must have been." She laughed at his expression. "Poor Jake, you aren't used to such treatment, are you?"

"I guess not," he admitted, grinning ruefully.

"Your poor mother." She smiled. "Do you have any brothers and sisters?"

"Two sisters and one brother, all of them younger than me. My youngest sister, a surprise to us all, is only a year older than you."

"Have you known Mr. Weston long?"

"Yes," he answered tersely. "Do you want to know my whole life story?" he asked impatiently.

"I wouldn't mind." She wouldn't be daunted by his change of mood.

He took her glass of wine out of her hand. "Well, you aren't going to. I have much better things to do than talk about my life." He touched the knotted front of her bikini in the center of her breasts. "Does this really hold this top together?" he asked huskily.

"Yes," she said breathlessly, unable to move.

"Mm," his fingers played with the material. "Very tempting."

"It isn't meant to be." She couldn't repress her shivers of delight as his fingers lightly brushed her midriff. "And I would prefer it if you aren't tempted."

"Not even a little bit?"

She swallowed hard. "No."

"But I can't help it." His arm clamped around her waist. "I think that so far I've behaved myself very well with you. I'm not usually this patient."

"So far?" she echoed softly. "Does that mean you're running out of patience?"

He bent his head to caress her throat with gentle lips. "I could be," he murmured. "Would you mind?"

"I don't know," she answered truthfully.

"You're a sweet child. But I don't think of you as a child!" he said with a groan. "Can I kiss you?"

"Do you need to ask?" Her big green eyes were fixed on his compelling face.

"I think so."

She wanted him to kiss her, she wanted it very much. "Then the answer is yes."

She raised her face for his kiss, her mouth opening under the pressure of his. It didn't seem to matter anymore that she had only met him yesterday. After all, if he had been someone of her own age, one of the crowd, she wouldn't have thought anything of them sharing a few kisses on their day out together.

But these weren't ordinary kisses, not the light caresses she could expect to share with other boyfriends she had had. These kisses were piercing the whole of her being, Jake's mouth devouring her until she felt dizzy.

She lay back on the blanket, Jake's body half lying over her as he continued to kiss her. Her arms were up about his neck, her fingers tangled in the thick dark hair at his nape. His hands were moving caressingly over her body from breast to thigh, but not once did he attempt to touch the fastening to her bikini again.

He raised his head to look down at her, his eyes dark with his arousal. "Now tell me that Matthew Day means something to you," he ordered gruffly.

"Matthew who?" she asked dreamily, lost in the vortex of her own passion.

He smiled his satisfaction, caressing her lips apart with his fingers. "Matthew Day," he murmured. "The man you've known for three years; the man you lived with for a time."

Her eyes widened. "Are you jealous, Jake?"

His lips gently parted and probed hers, his tongue caressing. "Insanely," he admitted against her mouth.

"You needn't be." She trembled, her body on fire for him. "Do I have the right to be jealous of your other women?"

He lifted his head. "There are no other women," he said indignantly.

"Your *past* women," she amended, her fingers lightly playing with the hair at his temple.

"Not when they are in the past, no."

"Matthew is part of my past."

His mouth tightened. "It isn't the same thing at all."

"It isn't?" she asked innocently, revelling in her power to make him jealous. "I thought it was exactly the same."

"You're nothing but a teasing little...." His hands tightened around her waist.

She raised her eyebrows. "Yes, Jake?"

"Little *wanton*!" he finished firmly.

She laughed huskily, touching several strands of gray hair she had just discovered at his temple. "You haven't exactly lived a life of innocence, not if these are anything to go by."

"Do I look as if I have?" he taunted.

"No," she answered truthfully.

"Well, I haven't, and I'm not about to claim otherwise."

"Why have you never married?" she asked curiously.

He frowned. "Who says I haven't?"

Her eyes widened. "You mean you have?"

"Would it make a difference?"

She gave a nervous laugh. "Of course it would."

Jake moved away from her to lie on his back. "Why should my being married make any difference to us being here together?"

She sat up, looking down at him searchingly, his expression unreadable as he met her gaze unflinchingly. "You really don't know?"

"You mean it does matter to you?"

"If you're married, yes!" she said heatedly.

"Why?"

She frowned. "Why? Because I don't go out with married men, that's why!"

"Okay, so I'm not married."

"What does that mean?"

He sighed. "It means that I want you to go out with me."

"Yes, but, that...that doesn't answer my question." She sprang to her feet. "You are married, aren't you? You have that look about you," she accused.

He watched her with amused blue eyes. "Browbeaten and trapped?" he taunted.

Stacy began collecting her things together, throwing everything into her handbag with agitated movements. "No, I wouldn't say that," she muttered angrily. "Just a...a *married* look."

Jake stood up, too. "What are you doing?" he demanded.

She glared at him. "I'm packing up to go back to the hotel," she snapped. "I should have realized." She picked up her towel. "I suppose everyone else at the hotel knows you're married, that's why you have this thing about being alone with me."

He touched her bare arm. "It isn't that at all, Stacy. I—"

"Oh, yes, it is," she cut in vehemently. "I should have known." She laughed bitterly. "God, I've really made a fool of myself this time. I'm too trusting, too impetuous, that's my trouble. Just look at you—sophisticated, handsome, oozing self-confidence. Why should you be interested in someone like me? I've been asking myself that all day—and now I have my answer. I'm naive enough not to even think of you being a married man!"

"Stacy!" He shook her hard. "I'm not married!"

She wrenched away from him. "I don't believe you."

"I was married, I admit that, but I'm not now."

That halted her angry movements. "So you aren't married now?"

"No." He shook his head.

She bent down to fold up the blanket. "I still want to go back to the hotel."

"There's no need—"

"There's every need!" she said fiercely. "I don't want to be here with you any longer."

"Come on, Stacy," his voice cajoled. "There's no need to be like this. I admit I shouldn't have teased you like that, but I really didn't mean to upset you. I didn't realize you would take it so seriously."

"Oh, I'm not upset," she told him sarcastically. "I enjoy being told by the man who just kissed me that he's a married man."

"Past tense, Stacy— *was* a married man."

"You didn't say that."

"I never once said I was married," he told her patiently. "Not once. You were the one saying that."

"I'll wait for you on board." She began wading out to the boat, leaving him to carry the rest of the things back.

Within minutes he had joined her, starting the engine without a single word. Stacy watched his rigid profile with resentful eyes, pulling on her slacks and top before sitting hunched up on the seat.

Jake gave her a brief look. "I take it you aren't going to talk?"

"You take it right," she said stiffly.

"Does that also mean you won't have dinner with me tonight if I ask you?"

"Somewhere conveniently far away from the hotel—and anyone who might know you?" she sneered.

"I did have a quiet little Italian restaurant in mind," he agreed. "It's—"

"Spare me the details. I'm not about to go anywhere with you. I don't trust you."

"I'm not married, Stacy," he said with a sigh.

"So you said." She refused to look at him.

"Oh, hell, Stacy! Why won't you believe me?"

"Can you think of any reason why I should?"

"So you won't come out to dinner with me?"

"No." She shook her head. "But I thank you for today. Most of it was enjoyable."

"I'll bet," he drawled. "You certainly are a temperamental little thing."

"Aren't I just?" she agreed sneeringly. "I warned you about making a fool of me."

"So you did," he acknowledged softly.

There didn't seem to be much else to say and so they drove back to the hotel in silence, Stacy getting hurriedly out of the car, not waiting for Jake. But he soon caught up with her, so that they entered the hotel together.

"Stacy," he said huskily. "Stacy, listen to me. I'm sorry about this afternoon. I should have told you, I suppose. It's just that my marriage isn't something I like to talk about."

"Well...." She could feel herself weakening toward him. "I—"

"Mr. Weston?" A young page was coming through the reception area. "Mr. Weston—" he looked straight at Jake. "—there's an important telephone call from your publisher. He's called three times today already."

Jake nodded distantly. "Thank you. Have them transfer the call up to my suite in a couple of minutes."

"Yes, sir."

Stacy gulped, waiting until the young boy had left before speaking. "*You're* Jake Weston?"

He took a deep breath. "I'm afraid so."

CHAPTER FOUR

SHE GAVE HIM a furious look before turning on her heel and marching over to the elevator. Jake *Weston*! *He* was Jake Weston! God, she was an idiot. She had been so convinced that Jake Weston would be fat, bald and ugly that she hadn't for one moment connected the lean, handsome Jake with him.

And he knew it, damn him! He had known of her mistake from their very first meeting, had overheard her conversation with Matthew and known of her error—and he had deliberately made a fool of her.

She felt herself wrenched around and looked up into the face of the man she now knew as Jake Weston. "Let go of me!" she ground out angrily.

He refused to be shaken off. "It isn't what you think, Stacy," he told her almost pleadingly. "Just let me explain."

"Explain what?" Her eyes flashed. "That you've been making a fool of me? Jake Weston, indeed!" she said with disgust. "And everyone else knew about it."

"There was nothing to know."

"Nothing to know!" she spat at him. "I spent all of yesterday evening and today with the famous Jake Weston, and you say there was nothing to know." She gave a bitter laugh. "I think there's plenty to know."

"Okay." He thrust her inside the elevator. "You can come with me and I'll tell you." He was angry, too, now.

"Wh—where are you taking me?"

"To my suite," he snapped. "I have to answer that telephone call, remember?"

"From your publisher," she scorned.

"Yes," he sighed.

"And I thought you were just an employee like me," she replied disgustedly.

His gaze raked over her coldly. "I still have to work for my living."

"But you're rich enough not to."

"I may be." He pushed open the doors and marched her down the corridor to his suite, throwing open the door and ushering her inside. He locked the door after him, putting the key in his pocket. "Now wait there while I make this call." He went into what she presumed to be a bedroom.

Stacy wandered into the lounge, aware of the luxury all around her. This was nothing like the tiny bedroom and bathroom she shared with Juliet. The luxurious leather sofa and armchairs and fitted deep pile carpets were only part of what must be a four- or five-room suite.

She was out on the balcony when Jake came out of the bedroom, the view of the hotel garden and grounds much better than the view of the parking lot she had. She turned as he came to stand beside her. "Would you mind unlocking the door now? I want to shower the salt out of my hair and off my body."

"And I want you to listen to what I have to say," he said, as if that ended the argument. "Come inside—we can talk better in there."

She brushed past him, her mouth set mutinously. "And just what did you want to tell me? That from time to time you like to pretend you're someone else? Perhaps you were even using me as research for your next book? I hope I proved suitable!"

"Stacy—"

"Yes, *Mr. Weston*?" she asked shrilly. "What can I do for you, *sir*? I suppose I should call you that. After all, it's because of your influence that I still have a job."

"You're right for the part of Kate," he said impatiently. "I wasn't going to let Payne ruin the film just because of a whim of Paul Forbes to get you into his bed."

"So you decided to try and get me into your own bed! Even Paul Forbes wouldn't argue with *you* about it—he knows better. And the man I thought was Jake Weston last night, who was he?"

"Brad Delmain, a friend of mine."

Her mouth turned back. "How convenient that he should exactly fit my picture of you."

"That was purely coincidental."

"I'm sure it was—and the joke was on me."

"I didn't deliberately set out to deceive you," he told her coldly. "You thought I was an employee of Jake Weston and I—"

"You thought it would be amusing to let me go on thinking that," she finished bitterly. "I'm only sorry that poor innocent boy ruined your little game for you, because I can assure you that you aren't going to play any more tricks on me. You're worse than Paul Forbes as far as I'm concerned. At least he was completely honest about what he wanted."

"I only wanted—"

"You wanted to find out how us lesser mortals live," she spat at him. "Only you got found out too soon."

"Shut up, Stacy," he snapped.

"I will not!" she said furiously. "I only hope your research was worth it, Mr. Weston. I look forward to seeing your next book; I may even have a major role in it."

"You won't," he said abruptly.

"Then you *did* get found out too soon. No wonder you

said I was completely natural with you. I may not have been if I'd known who you really were."

He looked at her through narrowed eyes. "I haven't particularly noticed any difference in your attitude," he pointed out dryly. "Your temper still seems to be as heated."

"And what else did you expect?" she taunted. "That just because I've found out your real identity I should suddenly start to be subservient? I may have been if I had known who you were when we first met, but not now, not now that I know you for exactly what you are."

"And that is?" he asked deceptively soft.

"A liar!" she told him fiercely. "A liar and a cheat. You would have seduced me this afternoon with no feelings of guilt, even though you were deceiving me about your very identity. I don't call that the action of an honorable man."

"You're beyond reason at the moment," he said with a sigh. "We'll talk later, when you've had time to calm down."

She walked angrily to the door. "We won't talk later, or at any other time for that matter. I would rather go out with Paul Forbes than you. He may be a flirt, but at least he's honest about his intentions."

"So was I!" He swung her around, his fingers digging painfully into the fleshy part of her upper arm. "I told you last night that I wanted you; I never pretended otherwise."

"You just had no intention of telling me who I would have the honor of sleeping with!"

"Oh, hell!" He ran an agitated hand through his thick dark hair. "You're completely misunderstanding my reasons." He turned away from her to pace restlessly up and down the room. "I don't know how to explain all this without sounding the conceited swine you already think me."

"Don't even bother to try. Just open the door and let me out of here."

"No," he refused sharply. "You could at least listen to what I have to say to you."

Her mouth thinned. "All right, go ahead. But I doubt it will change anything. I don't even know why you want it to; there must be dozens of women in this hotel alone who would be only too happy to go out with Jake Weston, to be seen with him."

"Exactly," he said with satisfaction.

She looked at him sharply. "What do you mean?"

"That women like to be seen with me. Because of who I am, what I am, women have always been in great supply. But with them I could never be sure if it was me they were attracted to or the glamour they seem to attach to my profession. When you didn't realize who I was I decided to keep up the pretence. I would have told you the truth when I was more sure of you."

"Last night I can perhaps understand, but today I can't forgive. I would have found out later today, anyway; my friends would all have been agog with my success."

"I would have told you myself over dinner this evening," he said with a sigh.

She gave a short laugh. "You can say that now, now that you've been found out." She turned back to the door. "I'm still waiting to leave," she told him pointedly.

He turned her roughly, pulling her into his arms. "You aren't going anywhere," he said forcefully, "except into my arms."

She struggled against him, once again feeling his sensual magnetism weaving its spell about her, aware of the hardness of his body pressed unyieldingly against her own. "Let me go," she ordered through gritted teeth, her panic clearly written in her eyes. "Let me go!"

He shook his head. "No," he said huskily, holding her flaying arms with arrogant ease. "I have no intention of letting you out of this room until I've convinced you that I wasn't playing some sort of sick joke on you."

Stacy looked up at him with challenge in her green eyes, her arms held firmly behind her back by just one of his. "And how do you propose to do that?"

"Like this." He groaned, his hand moving to hold her chin and so keep her head immobile as his mouth plundered hers with ruthless insistence.

Stacy obstinately kept her mouth closed, no longer fighting him, but having difficulty trying to resist the seduction of that firm caressing mouth. He was an expert when it came to evoking a response and she had almost weakened when he finally lifted his head to look at her with deeply blue eyes, his own arousal unmistakable.

"Kiss me, Stacy," he commanded softly. "Open your mouth and kiss me!"

She shook her head in obstinate refusal. "I can't stop you, Mr. Weston, but I certainly don't have to make it easy for you. You're accomplished at this sort of thing," she sneered. "I'm sure you aren't going to let the refusal of one almost unknown actress stand in the way of your own egotistical demands."

His eyes sparkled with suppressed anger and his mouth descended on hers with ruthless determination. This time he was giving her no chance to resist him, forcing his tongue between her lips and deepening the intensity of the kiss.

As the fight ebbed from her body he released her hands from behind her back, threading his own hands into her shimmering hair and making it impossible for her to evade that punishing mouth. Her legs seemed to buckle beneath her and she clung to his broad shoulders to stop herself from falling.

It was the hammering on the door behind them that finally broke them apart, Jake turning to glare resentfully at the door. "Who is it?" he rasped coldly.

"It's Brad, Jake. Can I come in?"

"Wait a minute," he growled at the man. "Don't leave, Stacy. I'll get rid of him." He took the key from his pants pocket, unlocking the door.

Brad Delmain, the man she had thought was Jake Weston, came into the room. "What's the idea of locking the door? Are you—Oh!" He seemed to become aware of the red-faced Stacy for the first time, looking apologetically at his friend. "Am I interrupting something?"

"Yes—"

"No!" Stacy picked up her handbag. "You aren't interrupting a thing. Excuse me."

Jake followed her, moving in front of her to block her way. "Will you meet me for dinner?" he asked softly.

She looked at him in amazement. "You have a nerve!" she snapped.

"Will you?"

"No, I won't," she said angrily. "I don't like you very much, Mr. Weston. I've already explained my reasons." She brushed past him and ran down the stairs.

She couldn't hear anyone following her and so she slowed down her pace. It still seemed incredible to her that she had actually been out with Jake Weston, been kissed by him, and not even known it. No one was ever going to believe her ignorance of his identity—she wasn't sure she believed her naiveté herself—his name had been a dead giveaway.

By the time she had showered and washed her hair it was getting on toward dinner time. Juliet came in about six-thirty, her eyes speculative.

"Have a nice day?" Stacy decided to play it cool.

"Did *I* have a nice day?" Juliet returned pointedly.

"Well, did you?" Stacy ignored her dig.

"Lovely, the weather has been perfect. But I'm more interested in how you spent the day." She sat down on her bed, looking at her expectantly.

Stacy shrugged. "I went to the beach."

"But not alone."

She sighed. "No, not alone."

"Now, come on," Juliet cried. "Put a bit more enthusiasm into your voice when you talk about spending the day with our famous author." She grinned. "You should have seen the green faces last night when you walked off with the prize of the evening."

"I'll bet," Stacy said dryly, vigorously brushing her hair in an effort to dry it. The long red tresses might look beautiful but they were certainly hard work, although she knew it had helped her get parts, especially the role of Kate in this film.

Juliet's face was full of excited interest. "Well, tell me about it. How did you manage to captivate him?"

"I didn't know I had," she said irritably.

Juliet spluttered with laughter. "You have to be kidding! He made straight for you as soon as we got to the party. Matthew was quite put out about it."

Matthew! She had almost forgotten about him, Jake Weston's forceful personality taking her over completely. "He needn't be," she remarked calmly. "I doubt I will be going out with Mr. Weston again."

"You won't?" Juliet's eyes were wide.

Stacy evaded those eyes. "I doubt it."

"But why? I'm sure he was completely enthralled with you. The way he came over to you was almost as if you already knew each other. And another thing, you seem to have your job back. His influence?"

Stacy's cheeks stained red. "I suppose so, although it isn't like you think," she added hastily.

"I'm in no hurry—tell me about it."

She shrugged. "There isn't much to tell. Mr. Weston just didn't agree with Martin Payne's decision to sack me."

Juliet grinned mischievously. "I'll bet he didn't," she teased.

"Juliet, please!" she said sharply. "Look, until a few minutes ago I didn't even realize he *was* Jake Weston."

Her friend looked exactly as she had expected her to look, disbelieving. "Everyone knows who he is," she said scornfully.

"Well, I didn't," Stacy said crossly. "And neither did Matthew last night."

"He does now. He's furious about the way Mr. Weston commandeered you."

Stacy looked surprised. "I don't see why; Matthew and I are only friends."

"I think he may have changed his mind about that; he's absolutely green today."

Stacy stood up impatiently. "He's just being ridiculous. It didn't work out between us before and as far as I can see neither of us have changed. I don't see why he's acting the jealous boyfriend."

"It's probably seeing you with someone else that's done it."

"He's seen me with other men before."

"But no one like Jake Weston."

Her eyes sparkled angrily. "Just the sound of his name makes my blood boil."

"Am I allowed to ask why?" Juliet was obviously filled with curiosity.

Stacy sighed, telling her of Jake's deception. "He says he

did it because he wanted me to like him for himself. I don't believe him."

"Mm." Juliet looked thoughtful. "It is a strange thing to do."

"Strange!" Stacy burst out. "It's downright stupid. As soon as we got back to the hotel one of the staff gave him away. I was already angry with him, but that just about finished me off."

"You were angry with *him*?"

She nodded. "Just another of his little jokes. He was teasing me about whether or not he's married."

"Oh, he is," Juliet said unhesitatingly.

Stacy paled, sitting down on the bed abruptly. "He is?" she asked dully.

"Oh, yes. That was another reason Matthew was furious. I was a bit surprised myself, but I— Hey." She noticed Stacy's stricken look. "I thought you said he had told you about his marriage?"

She shook her head. "He said he was married but that he isn't now."

"Well, maybe he isn't. We don't get all the gossip over here."

"Don't make excuses for him, Juliet," Stacy cut in. "It's just one more lie he's told me."

"But I could be wrong," Juliet insisted. "Don't blacken the poor man's character just because of something I've said."

Stacy shook her head. "He put the suspicion in my mind first. He didn't seem to think it mattered whether or not he was married, didn't see what possible difference it could make to us going out together. He only told me he wasn't married because I told him it did matter to me."

"Oh, dear, I think I can see now why he isn't very popular with you."

"He's decidedly *un*popular."

"Oh, well." Juliet grinned. "It will make one person happy, anyway."

"It will?"

"Mm. Matthew. The way he's boiling over right now I think he might even propose."

"Oh, no." Stacy's face showed her dismay. "That's the last thing I want."

"I thought you liked him."

"I do, as a friend. Anything else was over between us long ago."

"I see," Juliet said slowly. "In that case, perhaps you wouldn't mind helping to convince him that I'm more than just one of the crowd. He doesn't even seem to realize I'm feminine most of the time," she grimaced.

"I didn't realize...."

"That I like him?" Juliet finished. "You weren't supposed to. I don't go around pinching other girls' boyfriends."

"You wouldn't have been doing that."

"No, but I didn't realize that. If you could have seen how angry he was when he got your message this morning, you wouldn't be in any doubt as to his concern for you."

"Concern, yes." Stacy nodded. "But I'm sure you're wrong about him feeling anything else. We've been friends a long time."

Juliet looked uncertain. "Do you really think that's it?"

Stacy squeezed her hand. "I'm sure of it. And we'll have to see what we can do about you and him."

"And you're definitely off Mr. Weston?"

She wasn't "off" him at all. He was fascinating, had made her feel that she was the most attractive woman in the world to him. But he probably made every other female he met feel the same way—including his wife! He was an out-

and-out rake, and she would have to forget him. If only she didn't still find him so attractive!

"I won't be seeing him again," she answered evasively. "At least, not intentionally."

"He *is* the story consultant."

"I know that," Stacy said sharply. "That's why I said it wouldn't be intentionally. I can't avoid him if it's to do with the film."

"You do realize that now you're back on the payroll you'll have to go through the rape scene with the amorous Mr. Forbes?"

"Oh, no!" Her dismay was obvious. "I'd forgotten all about that." And with Jake Weston as the story consultant she would probably have him in the audience. God, how embarrassing, especially after the passionate kisses they had shared!

"I wouldn't worry about it," Juliet advised. "After Mr. Weston he should be easy to handle."

She nodded. "Like comparing a kitten to a tiger."

Juliet arched an eyebrow. "That bad?"

"That good," Stacy corrected derisively.

"Oh." Juliet grinned meaningly.

"Mm. I'm going to get dressed for dinner." She didn't want to discuss her reaction to Jake any further.

Juliet looked at her wristwatch. "Goodness, yes, it's getting late."

Stacy donned her emerald green dress, still very much with her thoughts on Jake Weston. Why had he lied to her like that, why? She had really liked him, and it was difficult not to be attracted to him. If only he weren't married, she might have forgiven him for deceiving her about his identity. But nothing could alter the fact that he was a married man—or that he had lied about it.

Matthew and Daniel were already seated at their table

when the two girls entered the dining room. Matthew stood up to hold out Stacy's chair for her while Daniel did the same for Juliet. "I wasn't sure you would be joining us," Matthew said almost resentfully.

She gave him a bright smile. "Why shouldn't I?"

"I thought perhaps you might be having dinner with Weston as well."

"As well?"

"As well as spending the whole damn day with him." He gave her an angry glare. "Honestly, Stacy, I couldn't have been more surprised if I'd been six years old and someone had told me there was no such thing as Santa Claus."

She licked her lips. "What do you mean?"

"I mean your going off with Weston like that. When he came back to the party last night without you everyone drew their own conclusions."

That he had gone back to the party was news to her; she had presumed he had gone up to his suite. But then, the party had been in his honor—even if she hadn't realized that at the time.

She met his gaze with clear green eyes. "Would you mind explaining yourself more clearly, Matthew? What am I supposed to have done?"

He snorted his disgust. "He went up to your room with you last night. It's pretty obvious—"

"Matthew!" Juliet cut in. "You really have it all wrong. Stacy didn't—"

"Please, Juliet," Stacy interrupted wearily. "Let him finish."

Matthew flushed angrily. "I don't think I need to bother. You know what everyone has been saying about you and Weston."

"I think so. You're all under the assumption that Jake came to my room last night, made love to me, and then calmly came back to the party as if nothing had happened. Leaving me in my room to sleep it off, I presume? Is that what you think happened, Matthew?''

"It isn't important what I think; everyone else thinks it."

Stacy sighed. "I'm not interested in anyone else's opinion. I want to know yours."

His mouth was a thin angry line. "You were with him today, too," he accused.

"So you agree with everyone else," she said resignedly.

"I'm not sure—"

"Oh, be sure, Matthew!" she snapped, rising unsteadily to her feet. "Excuse me." Her excuses were made generally, tears already blinding her vision.

She didn't care about the curious looks of the people she passed, wanting only to be alone. She escaped out into the garden, tears streaming down her cheeks. And they weren't all for the pain Matthew's mistrust in her had caused. Some of them were for the fact that she couldn't go out with Jake Weston again, not even if she wanted to. He was married and out of her reach.

She didn't see the man standing a few feet away from her, didn't know that he was looking at her, but she suddenly became aware of the smell of cigarette smoke. She hurriedly dried her cheeks before turning to look at this intruder into her pain.

Paul Forbes! She felt her heart leap nervously at this chance meeting with him, their first since she had refused to accompany him to the party the previous evening.

"Stacy?" He moved into the light to come toward her. "I thought it was you." He handed her a snowy white handkerchief. "Your cheeks are still wet."

She hurriedly wiped her cheeks, putting the handkerchief away in her evening bag. "I'll give it back to you when I've had time to launder it," she explained.

He gave a soft laugh. "And here was I thinking you were keeping it as a souvenir. But I should have known better, that sort of thing doesn't interest you."

She blushed, turning away. "I think I should go back inside."

Paul Forbes put a hand on her arm. "No, don't go. I wasn't getting at you, you know. In fact, I admire you all the more for refusing me."

She looked at him unflinchingly. "Is that why you had me sacked?" she challenged.

He shook his head. "I had nothing to do with that. I didn't even realize you had been sacked until Payne started muttering something about Jake Weston's interference in his decision."

"You really didn't know?" she asked uncertainly.

"No. And I didn't ask Payne to try and force you into going out with me, either. He did that from his own initiative."

"Oh." She didn't know whether or not to believe him. He sounded sincere and yet....

"It's true, Stacy," he insisted. "Oh, I know I have a lousy reputation, and most of it is true—but not all of it. And I don't resort to forcing women to go out with me."

She didn't suppose he usually needed to! He had always appeared to her to be totally conceited, using his fame to get him what he wanted. But it didn't necessarily follow that was what he had done with her. Maybe she had judged him too harshly.

"Mr. Payne gave the impression that you were behind his threat."

He was watching her closely. "And now that I've told you I wasn't?"

"If it's true, then I'm sorry I misjudged you." If it was true! His about-face was perhaps too good to be true.

"Have you eaten yet?" he asked softly.

She blushed as she remembered her flight from the dining room. "No," she admitted huskily.

"Would you have dinner with me?"

She hesitated. After all, this was Paul Forbes, the man she had claimed to despise. And she didn't like or trust him any better, that wasn't the reason for her hesitation. There was always a chance that Jake Weston would be in the dining room, and if he saw her with Paul Forbes he would know she had meant what she said about preferring the actor.

"It's only dinner, Stacy," he said persuadingly. "You would be doing me a favor," he added. "I'm not in the mood for a crowd tonight, and if people see you with me they're likely to leave us alone."

"Well...."

"Fine." He took her arm before she could accept or refuse, making her mind up for her. He smiled his pleasure, opening the door for her to enter. "Let's go. And don't forget I'm depending on you to help me keep my solitude, except for your lovely self, of course."

"Of course." She laughed at him.

She almost groaned out loud as she saw Matthew coming toward them. The last thing she wanted right now was another encounter with him. She turned away, pretending an absorbing interest in her companion.

But Matthew wasn't to be put off by that. "I've been looking all over for you, Stacy," he said almost accusingly.

She gave him a cool look, clinging all the tighter to Paul Forbes's arm. "Paul and I have been out in the garden."

Matthew looked at the older man. "I see," he said tightly. "Well, I really wanted to have a word with you in private."

"I'll just go and arrange our table, Stacy," Paul told her. "I won't be a moment." He nodded distantly at Matthew.

Matthew grabbed hold of her arm and pulled her over to a quiet corner. "What on earth are you doing with him?"

She gave him an innocent look. "I would have thought it was perfectly obvious. We're going in to have dinner."

"After what you said about him?"

She looked unperturbed. "We often make mistakes about people," she said meaningfully.

He had the grace to blush. "That's why I've been looking for you. Juliet told me of my mistake. I'm sorry."

"I accept your apology, but it doesn't really mean a lot. If it took Juliet to convince you of my innocence, then we aren't such good friends as I thought we were."

"Stacy!" He gave her a reproachful look. "I didn't for one moment think—"

"Oh, yes you did," she interrupted him angrily. "And no doubt your imagination is working overtime right now, too, about Paul Forbes and myself. Isn't it?"

"Well, you did say you despised him."

"And now I've changed my mind."

"You actually like him?"

"I don't know yet, do I? It may turn out that I do, but then again it may turn out that I don't."

He shook his head. "I don't know you in this mood."

"You don't know me at all if our last conversation is anything to go by."

"Perhaps you're right," Matthew agreed coldly. "First Jake Weston and now Paul Forbes! You're letting your popularity go to your head."

"Don't be ridiculous, Matthew. Having dinner with Paul Forbes doesn't put me under any obligation to see him again if I still don't like him." And it could tell Jake Weston what she thought of *him* once and for all.

"If you say so," he said distantly.

She looked at him appealingly. "It's only dinner, Matthew. If he turns out to be the louse we all think him then you can sit back and gloat over my second letdown of the day."

He sighed, stiffening as Paul Forbes rejoined them. "Just watch his hands, Stacy," he muttered warningly. "I hear he has about four pairs of them when he really gets going."

"I'll remember that," she promised, turning to smile at her escort as he came to stand at her side.

"Ready?" Paul Forbes gave her that heart-stopping smile that had been attracting the female fans to him for the last twenty years.

"Yes. I'll probably see you later, Matthew."

The dining room was very crowded when they entered, making it impossible for Stacy to see whether Jake Weston was here to be impressed or not.

"Paul?" Martin Payne's voice halted their progress, and they turned to look at him. He was seated alone at his table, and Stacy knew what he was going to say even before he said it. "Why don't you join us?" he invited. "I have some things I want to discuss with you, Paul."

Paul looked down at her. "Stacy?"

So much for his not wanting to be bothered with people! "I don't mind." She shrugged agreeably.

He pulled her chair out for her before sitting down himself. It wasn't until they were seated that Stacy realized Martin Payne had said "join *us*." She paled slightly as she saw the fourth member of their party making his way toward their table. Jake Weston! So much for the possibility of him seeing her with Paul Forbes!

CHAPTER FIVE

His blue gaze raked over Stacy being with Paul Forbes before he seated himself beside her. Stacy determinedly looked the other way.

"I thought it might be a good idea for Paul and Stacy to join us," Martin Payne explained to him.

"By all means." Jake nodded coolly. "I'm sure you must have a lot to talk to Paul about."

Stacy didn't like the way he grouped the director and actor together. She certainly didn't want to find herself talking to him all the way through the meal. As far as she knew they had nothing of interest to both of them to talk about.

She studiously ignored him all through the first course of the meal, but it seemed the director really did have a lot to talk to Paul Forbes about, making the silence between herself and Jake all the more noticeable.

"You didn't waste much time." Jake watched her over the rim of his wine glass.

She shied away from the intensity of his gaze, running one painted fingernail along the pattern on the tablecloth. "Didn't waste much time over what?" she asked innocently.

"Going out with Forbes," he said coldly, giving the man sitting on her other side a scathing look.

"I told you I preferred his honest intent to your lies."

"Yes, but—Oh, hell!" His mouth was a taut angry line. "You didn't have to go out with *him*, Stacy."

She appeared composed on the outside, although inside she was a seething mass of contradictory emotions, feeling attracted to him and yet fearing that attraction because he had a wife. "As I said, I prefer to know a man's intentions," she said coolly.

"And we both know his! God, Stacy, I told you my intentions from the beginning, too. At least with me you wouldn't have just been one of many."

"No?" She gave a harsh laugh.

"No." His hand covered hers under cover of the table. "I like my women one at a time."

Her green eyes flashed a warning of her anger and she pulled her hand away from him. "Then you should make sure you *do* only have the one!" she said in a fierce whisper.

His own eyes narrowed. "What's that supposed to mean?"

"If you don't know I'm not going to tell you." She turned away, sipping her wine.

"Stacy, will you—" He broke off as Paul Forbes turned to look at them.

Paul put his arm around her shoulders, bending his head close to hers. "Are you okay?" he asked softly. "Not bored or anything?"

She gave him a glowing smile, mainly for Jake's benefit. "Now how could I possibly be bored with Mr. Weston to entertain me?" she said sweetly.

Paul gave the other man a sharp look. "And is he—entertaining you, I mean?"

"Oh, yes. I only hope I'm not boring him."

Jake looked grim. "I'm sure Paul agrees with me when I say you're much too lovely to ever bore any man."

Paul's arm tightened about her shoulders. "Much too lovely," he agreed throatily, his eyes for her alone.

"About this scene, Paul," Martin Payne interrupted them. "I really do think we should sort it out before we get on the set tomorrow."

Once again the actor's attention was taken by the director and she was left to converse with Jake Weston. She couldn't help comparing the two men, and although Paul Forbes may be the film star, it was Jake who made the most lasting impression on the senses.

Both were dressed in black dinner suits and snowy white shirts, but there the comparision ended. Jake emitted a sensual magnetism and challenge to every woman in the room, his dark good looks much more preferable to Stacy than the blond insipidness of the other man. Jake also carried himself with a natural elegance that the other man could never hope to achieve.

Stacy brought her thoughts up with a start, not wanting to find Jake attractive. Paul Forbes may not exactly be any safer to be with, but at least he was single.

"Why are you here with him?" Jake demanded harshly.

She knew the other man's casual attempts to touch her had angered him, and she couldn't say she had liked his arm around her any more than Jake did. "He asked me."

"I asked you, too, but you turned me down."

"For obvious reasons," she said softly.

"They aren't obvious to me, damn you!" he rasped.

"Then perhaps they ought to be. Your dinner is getting cold, Mr. Weston." She pretended enjoyment in her own meal, although every mouthful was like sawdust to her taste buds. If she had known they would be dining with Jake she would never have agreed, although she thought Jake's presence had come as a bit of a shock to Paul Forbes, too.

Jake left his food untouched. "I'm not hungry," he

snapped. "And please don't give me a lecture on the starving millions. That I don't need."

"I wouldn't presume to lecture you on anything, Mr. Weston."

"Jake, Stacy. Call me Jake!" he muttered angrily.

"I wouldn't presume to do that, either."

"Don't try and freeze me off, Stacy. I haven't given up on you yet," he warned darkly.

"Then if I were you, I would do so." She patted delicately at her mouth with her napkin, leaving most of her food untouched, too. "I don't like you very much."

He sat forward, a slight smile curving his lips. "When I kissed you this afternoon you gave a very different impression."

"You mean when you *forced* me to respond."

"I didn't have to force you for long. If Brad hadn't come along...."

"The outcome would have been the same," she snapped. "Just because you've had plenty of practice at seduction doesn't mean that every female is going to fall for it. If your friend hadn't interrupted us I would have found some other way of getting away from you."

"Would you?" His eyes never left her face.

Stacy forced herself to look away. "Yes, I would! Could we talk about something less personal? I find this conversation pointless, to say the least."

"And I find you being here with Forbes most objectionable."

She raised an eyebrow. "Would you like me to leave?"

"Not you, *him*," he said forcefully.

"Anyone would think you were jealous, Mr. Weston."

"Anyone would be right!"

She flicked back her hair in a careless gesture far removed from her teeming emotions inside. "You have no right to be, no right to feel anything about anyone I should care to go out with."

"Not even if I care for you myself?"

She gave a short angry laugh. "Not that, please. I'm not that naive that I'll fall for an old line like that."

"And if it isn't a line?"

She shook her head. "The situation doesn't arise. Don't get the mistaken idea that a day out entitles you to more than just a thank-you at the end of the day. And I believe I've already said that."

"I can't believe you're seriously interested in Forbes," Jake said harshly.

"I'm not *seriously* interested in anyone."

"I'd like to change that," he told her softly.

It took great effort on her part to break away from the mesmerizing effect of his eyes. He had the most fascinating eyes, and they seemed to be becoming more and more so, reducing her to a weak and pliable woman who longed to be in his arms.

"No!" she said sharply. "No, Jake."

"Why not? We like each other, Stacy. I'd like you to get to know me better."

"I think I know all I want to know about you."

He was prevented from saying anything else on the subject by the other two men joining in the conversation, making it more general. Stacy said little, concentrating on her wine to the exclusion of everything else.

"Does that meet your approval, Stacy?" Paul asked.

She looked at him dazedly. "Sorry?"

"I asked if you would like to go through to the ballroom?"

"Oh, oh, yes," she agreed hurriedly. As the largest hotel in the area it also provided what little nightlife there was in the immediate vicinity, hence the ballroom. Live music was playing there most nights—music for all ages as the hotel was open to the public in the evenings. "That sounds like a good idea."

He nodded to the other two men. "We can carry on this conversation in there."

Stacy's startled gaze clashed with Jake's deep blue brooding one. She had thought they were finally to leave Martin Payne and Jake, but it seemed she was wrong.

She felt slightly self-conscious entering the ballroom as the only woman in the company of three men, two of them certainly the most handsome men in the room, and Martin Payne commanded a certain amount of respect in his own right.

As Paul Forbes became recognized people started to crowd around them, the majority of them women. That Paul reveled in it was obvious by the way the charming smile lighted up his face, and he instantly entered into conversation with several of the women. Martin Payne stayed at his side, probably wanting to keep a watchful eye on the star of his film.

And so it was that she felt her elbow taken in a firm grasp and found herself led away from the crowd of people over to a secluded table. Jake sat beside her, his chair drawn up close to hers so that their legs almost touched.

"Now you know why I prefer to keep out of the limelight, prefer to keep my identity secret," he remarked derisively.

Stacy looked over at Paul Forbes as he lapped up the attention he was receiving. Most of the people weren't hotel guests and she supposed the local people had been quite excited at having a film crew and its stars staying in the district.

"Those people are only showing their appreciation of his talent," she defended.

"That sort of appreciation I can do without," he told her dryly, signaling a waiter to bring them drinks. "I like praise as much as the next man—I'm not immune to flattery—but I prefer my privacy to any amount of praise."

"So that you can play tricks on people as you did on me last night?" she accused bitterly.

He sighed. "I wasn't playing a trick on you. I've already explained why I did it."

"Oh, yes, I know that. But do you realize that by going back to the party you gave everyone the impression you had just left me."

He frowned. "But I had."

"I don't mean just left me," she said impatiently. "I mean...." She hesitated about actually putting it into words.

Jake gave a slow smile. "I think I know what you mean. And who thought that?"

"Everyone!"

"Nice friends you have."

She blushed. "That's what I told them. Why did you go back to the party? I assumed you to have gone to your suite."

"Believe me, I would rather have done that. But the party was supposed to be for me, so I could hardly just disappear."

"I suppose not," she admitted grudgingly. "I just wish I didn't come out of it with such a blackened reputation."

"Your friends really thought that you and I had been—"

"There's no need to look so amused," she cut in waspishly. "I don't find it in the least funny."

"I don't imagine you do." He handed her the martini and lemonade he had ordered for her.

"Then stop smiling!" she snapped.

"I was just thinking that as people already seem con-

vinced you've slept with me that you really couldn't be
thought any the worse of if you actually did."

She gasped. "You're incredible."

"Surely you can see my point?"

"And surely you can see mine." She slammed her glass
down on the table. "I don't want to sleep with you."

"You're magnificent when you're angry; really beautiful," he murmured.

"And you're impossible at all times." But she felt herself
weakening toward him. God, he was a charmer. And if only
he would stop looking at her with those mesmerizing eyes,
she might be able to get up and walk away from him. At the
moment she felt too weak to do so.

He smiled at her, his teeth very white against his tanned
skin. "Can I take you out of here before Forbes breaks
away from his adoring public?" he asked throatily.

Stacy quivered at the seduction in his voice, clutching her
glass to her with both hands. "I happen to be here with him."

He gave the other man a scathing look. "He appears to
have forgotten you."

She flushed. "He'll remember me in a moment." She
hoped! How humiliating if he just left her here with Jake.

"And are you satisfied with that?" He sat forward, his
dark head only inches away from her own. "Don't you
mind having to sit back and wait to be noticed?"

She shrugged. "He's a famous man; he has to pander to
his public." But not as much as he was doing! He had more
or less ignored her through dinner and now he had spent
almost half an hour chatting to flattering females. She knew
he had only asked her to join him for dinner, but she now
felt that he had tricked her into that. He didn't look any
more in need of help to keep his solitude than she did. He
certainly wasn't acting as if he wanted to get away from his
fans—the opposite if anything.

Jake ran long sensitive fingers down her cheek. "I'd rather pander to you."

She gave a short breathless laugh, her skin tingling where he touched her. "Your line in chat is as polished as his is."

His mouth tightened with displeasure. "It isn't a line," he snapped harshly.

He stood up abruptly and Stacy thought he was leaving, only to find herself pulled to her feet seconds later and dragged onto the dance floor. She reacted violently as he molded her body close to his to move slowly in time to the music. His hands were at the base of her spine, his thumbs moving caressingly over her lower back, and Stacy had perforce to put her arms about his neck.

"What on earth did you do that for?" she demanded crossly. "Couldn't you have just asked me to dance like any other man would have, instead of using brute force?"

Jake shrugged. "You would have refused."

"Yes," she agreed instantly.

"That's why I didn't ask you."

"Your arrogance is unbelievable."

"It wasn't arrogance, Stacy, although I do admit I have that, too. Forbes has just managed to break away from the public he pretends to despise so much, and so I decided to whisk you away before he came over and monopolized your attention."

She licked her lips. "What do you mean, pretends?"

"I mean that he really loves all that attention. He says he doesn't, but I can assure you he would be most upset if no one recognized him."

She could imagine he would be. "That was still no reason to make it impossible for me to do anything other than dance with you. I'm really not in the mood for this right now." She was too much aware of the taut outline of his body against her own to be able to relax and enjoy the music.

"It was the only way I could think of to get you into my arms," he answered truthfully. "Has Paul Forbes ever kissed you?" he asked suddenly.

"How dare—"

"Has he, Stacy?" His arms tightened painfully about her waist, bringing her even closer to him.

"No, but I expect him to," she added defiantly. It was true, he *did* kiss her in the film—in fact he did a lot more than kiss her.

One of his hands moved to run his fingertips over her parted lips. "I hate to think of him violating this rosebud of a mouth," he said softly.

"Well, I can assure you he's going to."

He continued that featherlight caress against her mouth. "I won't let him," he vowed fiercely.

"You won't be given the chance to stop him. I decide who kisses me and who doesn't. And will you stop doing that!" She pushed his hand away. "People are looking."

"I like to touch your mouth. It's the most I can do in here," he said impatiently, his hand returning.

"It's the most you'll do anywhere," she corrected him. "And I wouldn't be letting you do that if I didn't think it would cause too much of a scene to insist."

"Then we'll stay here all night. I'm certainly not taking you back so that you can let Paul Forbes maul you."

"And I'm not staying here any longer. They'll think it odd if we don't return to the table." And being this close to him was shooting her temperature through the ceiling!

"I would have thought you would have learned by now that I don't give a damn what other people think of me."

"Then try to think of me."

"Perhaps you're right," he admitted with a sigh. "But I don't like the woman I want being with another man, especially someone like Forbes. Even Matthew Day would be preferable to him."

"Matthew and I have had a slight disagreement."

He raised his dark eyebrows. "Over me?"

"Over you," she acknowledged.

"He didn't approve of your being with me."

"Neither did I when I found out the truth about you." She had never gone out with a married man before, and she hadn't gone out with this one knowingly.

"It really makes that much of a difference to you?" Jake probed.

"Did you think it wouldn't?"

"It didn't occur to me."

She shook her head. "A thing like that isn't easy to ignore."

He shrugged. "It's never caused me problems before."

"I don't suppose it has," she retorted calmly. Not all girls would be put off by his married status.

"But it bothers you?" he persisted.

Of course it did; it would any self-respecting woman. "Yes," she said softly.

"Then there isn't a lot else I can say—except perhaps for you to be careful of Forbes. I told you up front what I felt, what I wanted; he has a much more underhanded way of doing things."

What could be more underhanded than a married man deliberately lying about his marriage! "I'll bear that in mind. But you really have no need to warn me about him. I've only had dinner with him."

"I hope that's all it remains," he said grimly.

Stacy gave a husky laugh. "Everyone seems to be warning me about him, and so far he's been nothing but polite to me."

"Who else warned you off him?"

She blushed. "Matthew."

"That boy has good judgment."

"He doesn't trust you, either," she told him teasingly.

Jake grinned. "Like I said, he has good judgment." He laughed softly, taking her hand in his. "Come on, let's go back to the others. You obviously aren't going to leave Forbes to come to me."

"As I'm not *with* Forbes, I can hardly leave him," she retorted. "But I do think we should return to the table." His hold on her hand was strangely intimate, and yet she felt bereft without the close hardness of his body as they danced.

She pulled her hand free as they sat down, waving to Juliet as she sat with Matthew a few tables down. At least Juliet had got her wish to have Matthew's attention, although by the brooding look on his face he wasn't very good company.

Paul Forbes followed the direction of her smile. "Is Juliet a friend of yours?"

Stacy turned to look at him. "We only met here, but as we share a room we've become quite good friends."

"You share a room?"

She laughed at his amazement. "We aren't all big film stars," she teased.

"Yes, but—I didn't realize you were actually *sharing* a room."

She shrugged. "It doesn't bother me. I'm glad of the company, actually."

"It's a bit restricting, though, isn't it?" he said thoughtfully.

Stacy frowned. "In what way?"

"Well . . . ." he gave a suggestive smile.

She blushed as she realized what he meant. "We don't have any of those problems," she told him stiffly.

"Oh, I see," he nodded. "You've worked out an arrangement."

"Certainly not," she said crossly, aware that Jake was watching her curiously, although Martin Payne was doing his best to hold his attention. "It hasn't been necessary."

His fingers ran caressingly down her bare arm. "We'll have to see if we can change that."

Stacy felt some of her old distrust of this man coming to the fore. What if his behavior earlier had all been an act just to get her to go out with him? She looked at him sharply. After all, he was an accomplished actor, and he certainly hadn't been acting like a man anxious to escape his public when they came in here. She knew with a certainty that she had been tricked for the second time that day.

She picked up her handbag. "If you'll excuse me, I'm feeling rather tired."

Paul also stood up. "I'll come with you."

"There's no need," she told him abruptly. "I don't want to spoil your evening."

His eyes were caressing. "You won't be doing that. I insist, Stacy," he said as she protested again. "I'd much rather come with you than stay here."

"Oh, all right," she muttered ungraciously. "Excuse me," she said to the other two men, evading Jake's searching gaze as he sought to catch her attention.

Paul grinned at the two seated men. "See you tomorrow."

Stacy held herself rigid as Paul Forbes refused to have his hold on her arm dislodged, finally moving away from him as they entered the elevator together. It was only when the elevator sailed straight past her floor that she began to panic in earnest. Jake had taken no for an answer, but this man was out to make a conquest, willing or unwilling.

"You've gone past my floor," she told him calmly, not

wanting to let him see just how panic-stricken she really was.

"I thought we could go to my suite and have a nightcap."

"We could have done that in the bar downstairs."

He shook his head. "Not with all those people about. Besides, I was getting a little tired of Weston ogling you."

She gasped. "He wasn't ogling me!"

"Oh, yes, he was. I don't know why you changed your mind about liking him, but I'm glad you did."

"I didn't change my mind," she protested.

"You must have." He stood back for her to precede him out of the elevator. "It's a sure fact that he still wants you."

Stacy colored brilliant red. "I don't want to talk about Mr. Weston."

"Neither do I." He unlocked his door and Stacy found herself in a suite very like the one Jake had. Paul closed the door softly behind her. "I'd much rather talk about you and me."

"Y—you and me?" she repeated stupidly, wondering how on earth she had allowed herself to be brought up here. She had been so busy protesting about Jake that she got herself into an even worse situation. "There isn't any you and me to talk about."

He poured out two glasses of whiskey, adding ice to hers before handing her the glass, his blue eyes intent on her flushed face. "Maybe not, but I'm working on it. Here." He pushed the glass toward her as she made no move to take it.

She shook her head, wishing there was more light in the room than the two side lamps he had put on at their entrance. "I don't like whiskey."

He shrugged. "Something else then? Bacardi, brandy, gin, vodka?"

"Nothing, thank you."

He put his own glass down, empty now. "I agree with you; we have better things to do."

Stacy backed away from him, fear clutching at her heart. "I'd like to leave, Mr. Forbes."

He laughed softly at her formality. "Not yet, Stacy. Not now that I've actually got you here. I don't like being thwarted, little girl," he added threateningly. "And you made a bloody fool out of me by going off with Weston last night."

"I—"

"You even got him to get your job back for you," he sneered, his face no longer good-looking, all charm leaving his voice. "After I'd told Payne to get rid of you."

Stacy paled even more. "*You* told him to. But you said—"

He gave a harsh laugh. "I know what I said...and you fell for it."

She saw it all now, now that it was too late. This man was just as much of a swine as she had thought he was. He couldn't bear the thought of another man having what he had wanted, so he had tricked her. He didn't even want her anymore, he just wouldn't be seen to be made a fool.

"You really are as awful as people say you are," she accused disgustedly.

He gave an ugly laugh. "Probably."

She walked angrily to the door. "Well, at least now I know. I won't be fooled again."

He swung her around. "After tonight you won't need to be. Once is all I want." His mouth descended on hers with cruel savagery.

Stacy fought against him for all she was worth, wrenching her mouth away. "Stop it!" she panted, fear in her eyes. "Leave me alone."

"Not until I've got what I want from you." His fingers

bit into the tender flesh of her arms, a determination in his face that would be hard to evade.

"You're disgusting!" She struggled with all her might, but he wouldn't be shaken off.

He laughed once more before claiming her mouth in the most punishing kiss she had ever received. He pinioned her arms to her side while taking his time over kissing her face and throat. "You might as well try to enjoy this, too," he growled.

Laughter choked in her throat, hysterical laughter. "No woman could enjoy being attacked," she said breathlessly. "You're hurting me!" Her mouth already felt swollen and bruised and there were dark bruises beginning to appear on the whiteness of her arms.

His narrowed blue eyes raked over her face. "Didn't Weston hurt you? No," he answered his own question. "I can imagine he has an altogether different approach."

"Yes! He doesn't need to resort to rape."

It was the worst thing she could have said. His mouth tightened into a vicious thin line, his lips moving to take hers with a punishing thoroughness. His arms were like steel bands around her, and all her struggling was futile against his superior strength. She was beginning to feel faint, all her strength deserting her. With one last desperate effort to escape him, she bit painfully down into his earlobe.

He let her go with a yelp of pain, putting up a hand to his ear as blood appeared on his shirt front. "You little bitch!"

The dark anger in his face frightened her and she ran quickly to the door. Before she had got half way there she felt the back of her gown caught in a firm grip, her determination to escape leading to the sound of ripping material as the thin shoulder straps gave beneath the pressure.

She wrenched open the door, holding the front of her gown up as it started to slip beneath her breasts. "You're an animal!'' She spat the words at him. "An animal!'' she repeated tearfully.

His mouth turned back in a sneer. "You don't look so appealing any more, do you, Stacy Adams?'' He slammed the door in her face.

She could imagine she didn't with her hair a tangled mess, her lips swollen, dark bruises on her arms and her gown in shreds. Oh, God, she hoped she could get to her room without being seen. She felt unclean, almost as if he *had* raped her.

As she turned to run toward the stairs she hit an immovable object. It was a man's chest.

She looked up with horror, raising frightened eyes. "Oh, Jake!'' Her relief was obvious as she collapsed into his arms. "Oh, Jake, help me!'' Deep sobs racked her body.

"My God, Stacy! What the hell happened to you?'' He held her at arm's length, looking down at the livid bruises on her flesh as she winced. "Forbes!'' he said forcefully. "Forbes did this to you?''

The tears were streaming down her face. "Yes,'' she gulped. "He...he—''

Deep burning anger flared in his eyes. "My God, did he—''

"No! No!'' she cried. "But it wasn't for want of trying.''

"The bastard!'' he swore. "I'll kill him for this. I'll kill him!''

She leaned heavily against him as he led her to his suite, her legs feeling incapable of supporting her. She was shaking so much her teeth seemed to rattle. Once inside his suite, Jake saw her seated on the sofa before moving to the liquor cabinet to pour her out a drink.

He held out the glass. "Drink it, Stacy,'' he encouraged as she shook her head. "It's brandy. It will calm your nerves.'' He forced the glass in her hand before moving to the door.

Stacy stared after him with bewildered green eyes. "Wh—where are you going?"

His face was white and grim as he looked at her. "I have to go and teach Forbes the right way to behave with a lady," he told her abruptly.

She put out a hand imploringly. "Don't leave me," she pleaded. "Please don't leave me, Jake."

He was instantly back at her side, pulling her head down onto his shoulder. The hand around her shoulders moved to gently smooth her hair away from her face. "What did he do to you?" he demanded harshly.

She shuddered, reaction beginning to set in. She licked her lips, conscious of stinging pain where the tender skin was broken. "He...he wanted...." She faltered as the memory of her narrow escape became all the more vivid. "He thought you and I had— He wanted the same—" She couldn't go on, burying her face in his throat. "It was horrible!"

Jake touched her swollen mouth. "And he did this to you because he thought that?"

She nodded. "And because he said he didn't like to be thwarted by any woman. He said I'd made a fool of him by being with you last night."

His mouth was tight. "He's made a fool of himself."

"He even tricked me into having dinner with him. He said I would help to keep the fans away, that I would be helping him," she added bitterly.

"I told you it was an act. But that warning came too late, didn't it?"

"Yes. I left when I realized he had been lying to me, but he insisted on coming with me. We were in his suite before I knew what was happening to me."

He shook his head. "You're too much of an innocent to see through his little act."

She nodded miserably. "I know that . . . now."

Jake stood up, his mouth a forbidding line. "Drink the rest of your brandy. I'll be back in a minute."

"You . . . you aren't going to see him?"

"I am," he told her grimly, the whiteness about his mouth evidence of his anger. "Just drink your brandy and I'll be back before you know it."

Stacy shivered. "I wish you wouldn't."

"I have to. I'll teach him a lesson he'll never forget," he promised fiercely.

He was back within five minutes, a look of satisfaction to his grim features. There wasn't a mark on him except for a slight redness to his knuckles. He sat down to pull Stacy back into the circle of his arms. "I don't think he'll be trying to rape anyone else for a few days."

Her eyes widened. "What did you do to him?" she asked breathlessly.

Jake gave a taut smile. "Don't worry, I didn't hit him anywhere it's going to show. He'll just have very bruised ribs for a few weeks. And a bitten ear, of course," he added teasingly.

Stacy blushed. "It was the only way I could escape him."

"He had a different story, but I soon shut his foul mouth for him." He seemed to control his anger with great difficulty. "Now, I think we had better do something about getting you to bed."

She looked down ruefully at her ripped dress. "I think I'm going to be a bit conspicuous going to my room like this."

"You aren't going to your room. You're staying here," Jake announced calmly.

CHAPTER SIX

HER PANIC-STRICKEN FACE was raised to his. Surely she hadn't escaped one sexual trap to get caught in another one equally as dangerous? Surely Jake couldn't be that cruel? "What...what do you mean?"

Jake sighed, giving her a reproachful look. "I mean that you're too distraught to go back to your own room. You can stay here where I can be sure you won't come to any more harm—for tonight, at least."

Stacy shuddered. "I won't ever be fooled by Paul Forbes again."

"You're so naive anyone could take you in...and does."

She struggled against him. "If you're just going to be insulting—"

Jake stayed her movements. "I'd like to do something completely different, but I think you've had enough for one night." He stood up, pulling her to her feet. "Come on, let's get you to bed."

She hung back. "I really don't think.... I share a room with Juliet—she'll keep me company until I can get to sleep." If she ever did! Memories of that attack would stay with her for a long time.

"She may not be back in your room, yet. I don't think you should be alone right now. I'll stay with you until you're asleep."

"But if anyone should find out...."

"They won't," he said firmly.

She gave in without any more fight, feeling safe here with Jake, which was strange considering her nervousness with him the last two days. But he was a man who would never need to resort to brute force, his charm and sensual magnetism making that unnecessary.

He took her into what was obviously an occupied bedroom. Male articles of clothing were scattered about the room, a box of cheroots lying on the bedside table.

She came up with a start. "I— This is *your* room," she accused.

"Sure, it's my room. I told you I don't want you to be alone."

"Yes, but—"

"It isn't what you're thinking, Stacy. You're going to get under the coverlet on the bed, and I'm going to sit beside you until you fall asleep."

"And where are you going to sleep?"

"I'm not; I'm going to stay here with you."

"But wouldn't it be easier—"

"You're staying here! I'm not having any more arguments." He pushed her down onto the bed, pulling the bedspread over her and switching out the light. "Now sleep."

She looked at him with huge green eyes. "You won't leave me?" she asked pleadingly.

"No." His hand firmly grasped hers as it lay on the coverlet. "Good night, Stacy."

"Good night." She watched him as he sat in the chair beside her until her eyelids began to droop and she finally fell asleep, his dark reassuring presence the last thing she saw before she faded off into oblivion.

She awoke once in the night screaming, sobbing until she felt hard comforting arms holding her tight, until she drifted off to sleep once again.

It was late in the morning when she woke up next,

stretching before sitting up in the strange bed. She gasped as the bedclothes fell back to reveal her nakedness. She was thankful that she was at least alone in her embarrassment. Jake must have undressed her in the night. But why? And where was he now?

She dived back under the covers as he came into the bedroom unannounced, looking darkly attractive in black trousers and a black fitted silk shirt.

"Good morning," he greeted cheerfully, placing a cup of coffee in her hands.

Stacy slammed the cup and saucer down on the table so that she could hold the covers over her naked breasts. "I'm not sure that it is," she said gruffly. "I— Where did you sleep last night?"

He shrugged. "In here. I told you I would."

She bit her lip. "And, er, how did I—"

Jake grinned. "How come you're stark naked?" He finished for her. "Well, you started ripping your clothes off in the middle of the night and so I—"

"I didn't!" she gasped. "I'm sure I wouldn't—"

"Apparently you thought you were being attacked again," he interrupted. "You had ripped off quite a lot of your things before I realized what you were doing. Then you just seemed to collapse back into a deep sleep. I thought you would be more comfortable without your ripped clothing and under all the bedclothes. You seemed more settled after that."

She blushed at the thought of him undressing her, although he seemed unperturbed, as if he were used to undressing women. Well, maybe he was used to undressing his wife and the other women he had in his life, but he wasn't used to undressing *her*.

"I wish you hadn't done that." She evaded his eyes.

He picked up the crumpled rag of her green dress. "I

didn't have much choice about it—you were nearly strangling yourself with this."

"You could have left my other clothing on," she accused.

"I did." He grinned. "A pair of the briefest briefs I've ever seen."

Her color increased as she realized he was right. The thin straps and fitted bodice of her gown had made it impossible for her to wear a bra, and a slip wasn't necessary with the underskirt. Her legs were tanned and smooth, making tights unnecessary, too. Oh, God, why hadn't she put more on!

Jake walked to the door with long easy strides. "I'll leave you to shower. You'll find a bathrobe behind the door in there."

"But what about clothes for when I leave?" She halted him at the door. "I can't go down in the elevator wearing only your bathrobe."

"You can tell me what clothes you want over breakfast, and I'll go down and get them. Your roommate should have left hours ago."

Stacy gave a startled glance at her wristwatch. "Ten o'clock!" she squeaked. "I should have been at work three hours ago."

"I telephoned Payne and told him you wouldn't be down there today," he told her calmly.

"You . . . you didn't!" But she knew he had by the indignation on his face at her doubt. She buried her face in her hands. "Oh, God, what will everyone think of me! Didn't Mr. Payne ask for an explanation?"

"He asked. I told him to talk to Paul Forbes about it."

"Which he won't," she said dryly.

"Probably not. He knows Forbes's tricks as well as I do. The only reason I didn't stop you leaving with him last night was because I thought you had more sense than to go to his room with him."

"I do!" she retorted. "It was because we were arguing about you that I didn't notice where he was taking me."

His blue eyes narrowed. "And why were you arguing about me?"

"Because he said you still wanted me—" She broke off in confusion as she realized what she had said.

"So?" he raised dark eyebrows. "I do," he acknowledged simply.

"You...you do?" she asked breathlessly.

"Would you like me to come over there and prove it?" he asked softly.

"No!" she said sharply, clutching the sheet even more tightly to her body. "No," she answered more calmly. "I must get showered and dressed and down to the location. I can't just take the day off on a whim."

"Payne said he wouldn't be needing you today. Besides, you're hardly filmable at the moment."

She put up a self-conscious hand to her bruised mouth. "Is it bad?"

"Well, it isn't pretty," he told her with cruel honesty. "You could possibly take the shots for after the rape scene. You wouldn't need any makeup."

Stacy paled at his cruelty, tears filling her eyes. "That was—that was—"

"Damned brutal!" he agreed harshly, coming back to stand beside the bed. "Oh, hell, Stacy," he groaned, sitting down to pull her close against his chest. "I didn't mean to hurt you. It's just that the thought of him...." He drew a ragged breath. "If he had succeeded I would have killed him."

He said the words with such calm ruthlessness that Stacy knew he meant it. She gave a shaky smile, his heart beating very fast beneath her fingertips. "You can't be any more relieved than I am."

Jake tilted her chin, looking deeply into her wide green eyes. "You don't know the half of it," he muttered huskily. "Stacy...." His lips gently touched hers. "Oh, Stacy," he gently lowered her back against the pillows, his mouth never leaving hers.

Stacy returned that kiss, the small amount of pain she was feeling as nothing compared to the pleasure he was arousing. After the vicious attack on her by Paul Forbes, she had no defences against Jake's gentle passion, finding comfort and reassurance in his arms, although she knew the gentleness of his caresses could just as quickly turn to hard demand.

The covers had fallen back and Jake smoothed her creamy skin with caressing fingers, cupping one of her breasts to bury his face against her, his tongue continuing the arousal of his fingers. "I want you, Stacy," he groaned. "I want you very much."

She shuddered as his lips claimed the tip of her breast, stiffening at the unfamiliar wave of emotion that suddenly racked her body. It was like nothing she had ever experienced before, a buildup of feeling that made her long for a release she wasn't even sure how to attain.

Once again it was the pounding on the main door of the suite that broke them apart, Stacy looking dazed and Jake looking slightly shaken, his eyes a deep glazed blue. "*God*!" he groaned, slowly moving away from her. "That must be the breakfast I ordered for us."

Stacy was so embarrassed now at the intimacies she had allowed him with her body that she just wanted to be left alone to shower and cover herself with whatever she could. "You had better let them in," she said softly, unable to look at his flushed handsome face.

He put a cool caressing hand against her hot cheek. "Yes, I think I'd better," he agreed huskily. "Would you like me to apologize?"

She turned away. "No. I'd... I'd like to be left alone."

"Yes." He stood up, running a hand through his already tousled hair. "I—you know what would have happened if they hadn't knocked on the door at that moment?"

"Yes."

Jake sighed. "Perhaps this isn't the right time to say it, not in the circumstances, not after what I just tried to do, but I want to protect you, Stacy."

Her eyes widened. "From what?" She could imagine nothing more terrifying than a repeat of the onslaught he had just made on her senses, her resistance against him nil.

His mouth twisted. "From Paul Forbes and men like him. But after what I just did I'm sure you see me in the same light as him."

"No, I—"

"Oh, hell!" He swore as the knock on the door was repeated. "We'll talk about this over breakfast, although I have to admit that I'm no longer hungry for food." His eyes caressed her, leaving her in no doubt where his appetite lay.

Stacy blushed, knowing a hunger to match his. "You should answer the door," she suggested.

"Yes. Yes, I suppose I should." He dragged his gaze away from her creamy shoulders. "Don't be long."

She could hear the murmur of voices as she showered and donned the bathrobe, shy about facing Jake again after the passion they had just shared. She didn't know why, but every time he touched her she seemed to melt against him, longing for an intimacy she had no experience of. Nothing had seemed to matter to her just now except that he go on kissing her, touching her, and after she had thought she would never want another man that near to her again. But she had wanted Jake to go on touching her, had wanted him never to stop.

Oh, God, if only he hadn't stopped, if only he had gone on kissing her and caressing her, had consumed her as her body had cried out for him to do. Then she would be in his arms even now, would know the full wonder of him, would have become a woman in his embrace, instead of which she now had a dull ache in the pit of her body, an ache that would remain with her until she could once again be in his arms. She loved this man, she knew it now, knew that she wanted to be with him for all time.

But he already had a wife, and even if he hadn't, desire was the only emotion he had expressed for her, a desire that would quickly fade after his possession of her.

There were dark shadows of pain under her eyes as she steeled herself to face him again, to meet his deep compelling eyes and try not to shy away.

Her head was bent down as she left the bedroom, the robe securely tied around her waist, although, being Jake's, it was far too big for her. She looked up to find that Jake wasn't alone; Brad Delmain was with him.

"Oh!" she gasped, deep color flooding her cheeks.

Jake stood up to come to her side. "Brad arrived with the breakfast," he explained softly, putting a protective arm around her shoulders.

Brad stood up with a shrug. "You should have explained, Jake. I wondered at your abrupt attitude. And then there were the two breakfasts. I should have realized," he finished lamely.

Stacy blushed anew, burying her face in Jake's chest. "Help me!" she pleaded in a muffled voice.

He cradled her to his side. "I'll get you some clothes; that should make you feel better." He smoothed her hair down her back, a livid red color against the white robe.

She huddled against him. "Don't leave me here," she begged.

"Brad's all right," he soothed gently. "This isn't like it looks, Brad," he spoke to his friend. "Don't frighten her while I'm gone," he warned. "Give me the key to your room, honey," he requested softly.

She moved with slow jerky movements to get her key out of the bag, reluctant to leave his side. The thought of going back to her room reminded her about Juliet. She would have some explaining to do about her absence last night when she saw her again.

"You won't be long?" Her eyes pleaded with him, her embarrassment very acute in the presence of the other man.

"No. Just tell me what to bring you."

"Any one of the cotton dresses in the wardrobe. Just enough to get me down to my own room. I don't intend going anywhere else today." She put up a self-conscious hand to her swollen mouth.

Jake removed her hand to touch her tender skin with his long, caressing fingers. "I didn't hurt you?"

She looked pointedly at Brad Delmain as he watched them with curious eyes. "No," she replied abruptly.

"I'll be as quick as I can. I only hope your roommate *has* left," he grimaced.

She hovered in the bedroom door once Jake had left, not sure what to do next.

"Come and have some coffee." Brad made up her mind for her. "You look as if you could do with some."

She came and sat down, taking the steaming cup of coffee he held out to her, wincing as the hot liquid stung her mouth.

"That looks sore," Brad commented.

"It is," she acknowledged, not enlarging on the subject.

"I hope I haven't interrupted anything," he continued without embarrassment.

"No," she denied sharply. "As Jake said, this isn't like it looks."

"I wasn't judging, Stacy," he said gently.

She gave him a sharp look. "How can you do anything else! You come here to see Jake, and I walk out of his bedroom clothed only in his bathrobe." And the briefest pair of briefs Jake had ever seen! "You can come to only one conclusion."

"Not necessarily...."

"Of course you can," she said angrily. "And you must have some opinion of me, staying the night in a married man's bedroom."

"Married man?" He frowned.

"Yes, married!"

"You mean Jake?"

"Who else?" She gave him an impatient look.

"Who told you he was married?"

"It's public knowledge."

Brad shrugged. "Then it's wrong."

Stacy looked unsure. "But he— Do you deny that there is a *Mrs.* Weston?"

He shook his head. "Was a Mrs. Weston."

Stacy gulped. "You mean he was telling the truth when he said he isn't married?"

"Yes. His wife is dead."

"Oh, dear," she said weakly. So she had misjudged him; he had been telling her the truth all the time. Oh, why had she listened to Juliet! Her friend had warned her she could be wrong.

"I'm his lawyer, Stacy, and I can say with certainty that he is no longer a married man. And it's because I'm a lawyer that I don't take circumstantial evidence as proof.

You came out of Jake's bedroom, but that doesn't mean he slept in there, too.''

"He did," she admitted. "But in the chair."

"And I believe you." He smiled. "But even if you had slept together it's nothing to do with me."

"You're very kind," she smiled shyly.

"Kind, hell! If it had been me instead of Jake, you sure wouldn't have slept alone."

She giggled at his teasing manner, liking this man in spite of his outrageousness. She was still smiling when Jake came back into the suite, her humor slowly dying at the scowl on his face.

He threw the dress at her. "Here," he snapped curtly.

She stood up. "I—I won't be long." She wanted him to look at her but he seemed to be avoiding doing so.

"Don't rush on my account." Still he didn't look at her.

"You can rush for me," Brad said easily. "I'll be devastated without you."

"Go and dress!" Jake ordered abruptly.

She went. Jake was angry and distant with her, just at a time she had found out *she* had no reason to be distant with him. He wasn't married and so there was nothing to stop her going out with him if he asked her to. Although his attitude just now hadn't pointed to him wanting to do any such thing.

When she came back out of the bedroom Brad had left. Jake was sitting alone on the sofa drinking black coffee. She blushed as she remembered the way he had touched her only minutes earlier, although there was no sign of their recent passion on his cold hard face.

"Brad had to leave," he informed her tersely.

"Oh," she said dully, unsure if he wanted her to go immediately or if he still expected her to have breakfast with him.

He gave her a narrow-eyed look. "Does that bother you?"

She met that cold assessing look for several seconds before turning hurriedly away again. "Why should it?"

He shrugged. "You seemed pretty friendly when I came back just now."

She couldn't believe it, Jake was actually *jealous* of the other man! If only he knew, he need never be jealous of any man where she was concerned. She was totally his. "Brad's an easy man to be friendly with," she told him lightly.

"Brad?" he questioned harshly. "It didn't take you long to get on a first-name basis with him."

As the lawyer had called her Stacy it hadn't occurred to her to call him Mr. Delmain. "It just seemed to come naturally," she excused.

"I'm sure it did," he said with a sneer. "Haven't you learned yet that it doesn't pay to take men at their face value? He could be another Boston Strangler for all you know."

"But he isn't, he's a lawyer."

"You seem to have found out a lot about him in a short time."

"Not really. And when you say I shouldn't take men at their face value, does that include you?"

"Especially me," he snapped. "You think I would have held back this morning if we hadn't been interrupted? I wouldn't," he answered his own question. "I once told you that I have never considered my age a barrier to going out with any woman, but now I think I could have been wrong. My age, the way I've lived, it all adds up to my not being able to indulge in just an emotional affair. With me it has to be physical, too. Your age against mine is a barrier against that."

"It doesn't have to be."

"Oh, yes, it does." He sprang to his feet. "But my offer to protect you still stands. You'll just have to excuse me if I have a few lapses like this morning. You're a very desirable young lady, and you only have to smile to shoot my temperature sky-high."

"And...and how do you intend to protect me?"

"By becoming your unofficial bodyguard."

She gave him a puzzled look. "I don't understand you."

"You need protection from Forbes. My hitting him last night won't have deterred him. You made a fool of him, and as he didn't succeed with you...."

Her eyes were green pools of fear. "You don't mean he might try that again?" She shuddered her revulsion.

"He *will* try it again," Jake said with conviction. "I just intend being with you at every opportunity. If he believes us to be having a heated affair he'll know not to come anywhere near you, but if we just go our separate ways again he'll make another move like last night."

Stacy felt sick at the thought of it. "I think it might be better for everyone if I left."

"No! Not for you, not for me, and why give Forbes the satisfaction of knowing he's frightened you away."

"But you...you can't want to spend all that time with me."

He gave her a tolerant look. "Don't be ridiculous."

"But it...it limits your social life to just me."

He shrugged. "Since I've been here the only social life I've wanted has been with you. Don't worry, Stacy. I'm aware that your response of this morning was made out of gratitude. I'm not saying I won't make a move like that again; I'm just saying that I know you have this aversion to who and what I am. That's never been a problem to me before, either," he added. "You're a funny kid."

He believed her to dislike *who* he was when in actual fact it had been his marital status that had frightened her off. But what could she say to disabuse him of that? She couldn't just turn around and say that now she knew he wasn't married, she would love to go out with him. She couldn't be that forward.

"I—I'd better leave now," she said huskily.

"Stay and have your breakfast," he ordered.

"No, I—"

"Stay, Stacy," he repeated curtly.

She did as he said, refusing to have anything but buttered toast and coffee. "Do you really think it will be necessary to protect me from Paul Forbes?"

He raised one dark eyebrow. "After last night do you doubt it?"

She remembered her pain and humiliation. "I suppose not," she admitted huskily.

"Right, well, I suggest that when you've been down to your room we go for a drive down to the location spot."

"Oh, no," she protested, putting up a hand to her mouth. "I couldn't face anyone looking like this."

"You can, Stacy, and you will. You don't think the bruising is going to be any less tomorrow, do you? I can assure you that it will be worse, the colors more livid. No, you'll face Paul Forbes today," he insisted harshly.

"I—I can't!"

"You will, Stacy. Besides, I do have work to do. Any problems they come up against I'm supposed to sort out. I only stayed back this morning because I thought you needed to sleep."

Stacy looked puzzled. "But you haven't been on the set the last few weeks."

"I was held up in America—something personal," he supplied abruptly.

"I see." She bit her lip. "But I don't have to come down there with you. I would rather not see anyone right now."

"That's precisely the reason you're going to. Come on, Stacy, you're an actress, a damned good one. Surely you can carry this off with some degree of pride."

"How do you know I'm a good actress?"

"I've seen your screen test hundreds of times."

"Oh, yes, I remember you saying Mr. Weston had seen it." She gave a wan smile. "That was before I realized *you* were Mr. Weston."

"Yes," he said tersely. "I think we've covered that subject enough." He looked at the gold watch on his wrist. "Can you be ready in fifteen minutes?"

"If I have to."

"You have to. You'll be seeing all these people tomorrow anyway. You can't just stay in your room." He gave a derisory smile. "If you're lucky everyone will think I did that to you; that my passion got a little too savage."

Color flooded her cheeks. "You don't really think anyone would imagine that?" she asked in dismay.

He shrugged. "I'm saying they could, and that perhaps it would be as well if they did."

"Oh, no." She shook her head. "I couldn't bear it."

"You would rather everyone knew Forbes tried to rape you?" he demanded harshly.

"No! But I—I can't let them think that you and I—that we—"

"Why not? Surely that's preferable to the truth? Or don't you think so? Would you prefer everyone to know the truth rather than have them think you slept with me?"

He was angry, cold chilling anger that she couldn't mistake. "I didn't mean that," she pleaded for his understanding.

"Then get yourself ready," he snapped.

"Jake, are you—why are you so angry with me?"

His blue eyes narrowed. "You were flirting with Brad in my absence." He didn't attempt to deny the emotion.

She gasped. "I wasn't!"

"Yes, you damn well were! And only minutes after being in my arms."

"I wasn't, Jake. Honestly. He was kind to me, that's all." And he had told her the truth about Jake's marital status, something she would always feel grateful to him for.

"And if I'm kind to you will you smile at me as you did at him?" He moved forward to grasp her forearms in a painful grip, pressing into her already bruised flesh. "Will you, Stacy?" he demanded.

"You're hurting me." She squirmed in his grasp.

"I'll do more than that if I ever see you smile at any other man like that again," he told her grimly.

Stacy looked up at him with startled green eyes, her red hair tumbling down her back. "What do you mean?" she asked tremulously.

Jake thrust her away from him. "Forget I said it," he ordered fiercely. "I'll meet you downstairs in ten minutes."

She hurried to her room, not wanting to anger him anymore. He had changed from the curiously gentle man to a man racked by jealousy. It gave her hope for their future relationship, although she didn't know how she could possibly show him how attracted she was to him when he could become so distant from her.

He had expressed desire for her and his reaction to her this morning had more than proved he still felt the same way, but he had the wrong idea about her morals. She realized she was to blame for that; she had told him she had lived with Matthew for a time, and she had behaved shamefully by spending the evening with Paul Forbes the night before.

If Jake knew just how attracted she was to him he might expect her to enter into an affair with him, and although she knew people in her profession were supposed to be promiscuous, she had never found that to be the case. And it certainly wasn't true of her. She may have been brought up in an orphanage, but they had taught her to have a moral code, one she had stuck to. Her wedding night would be the first time she knew a man in the full sense of the word.

It took her longer than Jake's stated ten minutes to make herself presentable. She couldn't help but feel shocked by the state of her mouth and arms. It had taken quite a lot of makeup to hide the dark marks on her skin, and her mouth still looked swollen, as if she had been kissed with great passion, as Jake had suggested. Although it was a hot day she had to change into a long-sleeved dress to cover up the purply bruises on her arms.

Jake was scowling by the time she met him downstairs. His gaze passed mockingly over the lip color that partly hid the discolored skin beneath. "That's quite a good repair job," he taunted, taking hold of her arm to lead her outside to the sports car.

"I did my best," she retorted sharply.

"Like I said, you did a good job."

"It was the *way* you said it, almost as if I invited that attack."

"I see your temper has returned with your composure," he mocked arrogantly.

"*Do* you think I invited what happened last night?" she demanded.

"Did you?" he quirked an eyebrow.

"Jake!"

"Then don't ask such damned stupid questions," he returned coldly.

There were plenty of people about to witness their arrival

when they reached the cove that was being used for filming. The two of them received more than their fair share of curious glances.

Stacy clung to Jake's hand as if it were a lifeline, never feeling quite so conspicuous in her life before. By the time they reached Martin Payne's side she felt as if her face was permanently red.

They were shooting some of the scenes with Juliet and were obviously having a little trouble, Martin Payne losing his temper with his male star. "For God's sake, Paul, you're supposed to be making love to the girl! You're moving about like a wooden doll."

Stacy caught Jake's grin of satisfaction and turned hurriedly away before her own humor began to show, too.

Paul Forbes turned a furious face on the director. "I'm sick and tired of doing this damned scene, that's why."

"Then you should have got it right the first time," Martin Payne rebuked. "All right, all right, let's take a break. Five minutes only," he added warningly, turning to look at Jake. "I don't know what you've done to him, but Paul has been damned impossible to work with today."

"Isn't he every day?" Jake returned dryly.

The director sighed. "Most days," he admitted. "But he can usually act—today he can't even do that. He's supposed to be making love, instead he holds the girl as if he's frightened to get near her."

Jake grinned. "That's probably because he is. It can't be all that comfortable when your ribs feel as if they're broken in a dozen different places."

"My God, you didn't actually hit him?"

Jake's grin widened. "And enjoyed every moment of it."

"Why the hell didn't he just say so? We could have shot something else today, instead of which I've wasted a whole morning."

"The circumstances behind my hitting him probably aren't something he wants to talk about." He looked down at Stacy as she squeezed his hand warningly. He was right, she would prefer people to think they were lovers than that Paul Forbes had tried to make love to her against her will. "All right, honey?" Jake's voice lowered intimately.

"Yes, I'm fine. I, er, I'll just go and have a word with Juliet," she said awkwardly.

"Okay," he nodded. "I'll look for you when I'm ready to leave."

She escaped as he and the director became deeply engrossed in discussing one of the scenes, slowly making her way over to where she could see Juliet in conversation with one of the other girls. She was almost there when she looked up and met the hate-filled eyes of Paul Forbes. She stopped in her tracks as he walked toward her with purposeful strides, his mouth turned back in a sneer.

CHAPTER SEVEN

STACY WANTED TO MOVE, to walk away, but she was rooted to the spot by her own fear. Last night this man had tried to rape her, and although she knew he couldn't hurt her in front of all these people, verbally he could rip her to shreds.

His fingers curled painfully about her wrist, the smile on his face in no way matching the venom in his eyes. "Smile, Stacy," he ordered, the pressure of his fingers increasing almost to breaking point. "We wouldn't want anyone to guess that we aren't the best of friends, now would we?" The smile remained fixed on his face.

"I couldn't give a damn what people think," she said fiercely. "You're despicable and everyone should know it."

"Know what, Stacy? That I tried to take you against your will?" He shook his head mockingly. "I don't think so, Stacy. You see, I would just have to tell them that you're a young girl who became infatuated with me, and like any red-blooded man I lost my head a little."

"And these bruises?" she sneered.

"A little too much passion," he returned calmly, unwittingly using Jake's excuse. "I think that in your case I would be the one to be believed. You see, Stacy, you've been a little too friendly with too many men of late."

She gasped. "What do you mean?"

"I mean Saturday night at dinner with Day, the evening spent with Weston, the next day with the same man surprisingly, and then dinner with me yesterday evening. And now today you're with Weston again. Not a pretty picture is it?" he taunted.

The way he put it, it did look pretty damning. "But I—"

"You what?" he scorned. "Tried us all out and found Weston the best in bed?" He shrugged. "I don't see how anyone would imagine anything else."

Neither could she! And for a girl who usually steered well clear of any sort of emotional entanglements, she seemed to have well and truly blackened her name over the last two days. "But Jake knows the truth," she insisted. "He—"

"Ah, yes, Jake." He looked at the other man as he talked to Martin Payne, apparently unaware of their conversation. There was pure hate in the look. "He may *think* he knows the truth."

Stacy gave him a sharp look. "What are you saying now?"

"I'm wondering how Jake would like to hear what really happened last night."

"But he already knows." She frowned her puzzlement.

"The truth as you tell it."

"But you know it's right! I wouldn't—"

Paul laughed, an unpleasant sound without humor. "Wouldn't sleep with me," he jeered. "Is that what you told Weston?" He laughed again. "I only have to tell him a different story to put the seeds of doubt in his mind. In fact I already made a start on that last night."

She swallowed hard. "You ... you did?"

"Sort of. I implied it may not have been all one-sided, that you liked a man to be rough with you. He didn't appear to take too much notice of me at the time, but I think I could persuade him that that's the way it happened if I cared to."

Stacy was very pale and she felt sick at the malevolence of the man. "Why should you want to do that?"

"Why?" Furious anger burned in his pale blue eyes.

"Because I don't take kindly to being beaten up by someone I consider no better than me, and because you cheated on me. And I could make him believe it, too, Stacy. A very jealous man is Jake Weston. I could tell him how you led me on and then—"

"I didn't lead you on," she burst out indignantly. "I had no intention of... of—"

"Perhaps you didn't, but before I'm finished I'll make sure Weston thinks you did."

"You're sick! You have to be to want to do something like this. One dinner with you doesn't mean I have to sleep with you."

"But you slept with Weston. Don't deny it, Stacy, I know it's true. Your friend Juliet unknowingly told me you hadn't stayed in your room last night." He smiled. "She was under the impression you had been with me."

She bit her lip. "I see," she muttered. "And why are you telling me all this?"

"I've had time to think of a suitable revenge on Weston for these bruised ribs he gave me—"

"And what of my bruises?" she interrupted angrily. "You were like a savage animal last night."

"Probably because that's what I felt like. I'm the star around here, girl, and I don't like kids like you thinking they can hog the limelight. As I was saying, I'll get my revenge on Weston, and I'll get it through you. He's a lot like me in some ways; he likes women but not marriage, but while a woman interests him she gets all his attention. Once his desire evaporates it's a different story, but then I don't intend waiting that long."

"Waiting for what?"

He smiled with malice. "I'm going to wait until he's reached the peak of his interest in you and then I'm going to tell him I've already had you."

"But you haven't!"

"He won't know that. You should know by now, Stacy, I tell a very convincing story."

"You would do a thing like that just because I turned you down?"

"I've done worse with less provocation."

"You're evil!" she said with feeling. "Evil and sick! You've started believing all the flattering things the press have to say about you, and when that happens you lose your own identity, as you're doing. I find it hard to imagine you were ever a nice person, but I suppose you might have been once. Do your worst, Mr. Forbes." She flicked her head back in a haughty gesture. "I couldn't give a damn what you do," she lied.

"We'll see," he taunted.

She stumbled away from him, feeling almost dazed by the hate he had managed to convey to her while the rest of the people standing about them seemed totally oblivious of the tension between them. At last she reached Juliet's side, she and another girl breaking off their conversation as Stacy joined them.

"I wish I knew how you did it," teased Anna.

"Did what?" Stacy asked lightly.

"Managed to captivate the two best-looking men here. I haven't even met Mr. Weston, yet, but he looks absolutely fascinating." She turned to Juliet. "I'll see you later."

"Well." Juliet grinned at Stacy. "You're turning out to be the center of attention."

"Things aren't always what they seem," she mumbled in reply.

"Have you seen Matthew yet?"

"No."

"He's back at the hotel somewhere. And you haven't seen him?" Juliet frowned worriedly.

"No."

Juliet whistled through her teeth. "Maybe it's as well. He was hopping mad last night. I don't know if he's calmed down yet."

Stacy frowned now too. "What's the matter with him?"

Juliet gave a shout of laughter. "What's the matter with him! As if you don't know," she chided.

"But I don't."

"Come with me to the caravan while I change," Juliet suggested. "For some reason Paul Forbes keeps muffing this scene and so they've decided to scrap it for today. I may as well get back to the hotel. Come on."

Stacy followed her over to the caravan that some of the lesser known actors and actresses occasionally used to change their clothes in.

"So," Juliet encouraged. "Tell me all about it."

She sighed. "What do you want to know?"

"All of it—as long as you don't think I'll be too shocked." Juliet laughed. "You've shocked poor Matthew out of his tiny mind. Personally," she added confidingly, "I think he's just piqued because he didn't have the same luck."

"As who?"

"That's what I want to know," Juliet said impatiently. "You left the ballroom last night with Paul Forbes and yet you turned up here with Jake Weston. The mind boggles!"

"Well, it needn't," Stacy sighed. "Neither of them had any luck with me."

"You have to be joking."

Stacy shook her head. "If Matthew's annoyed because he imagines I've slept with either of those men he can calm down, because I haven't."

Juliet looked disappointed if anything. "You mean he

spent the best part of the night sitting in our room chain-smoking for nothing?''

"If that's what he did, yes.''

"I don't believe it!''

"It's the truth, Juliet. I've already told you I don't go in for those sort of affairs.''

"I don't mean I don't believe you, I just meant I find it incredible. But if you say it's so, then it's so.''

"I wish everyone had your faith,'' Stacy said dryly.

Juliet shrugged. "You're bound to get a bit of jealous maliciousness. After all, as Anna said, you seem to have captivated the two dishiest men here.''

"Forgive me if I disagree with you about the last statement.''

"About the two dishiest men?'' Juliet raised her dark eyebrows. "Which one doesn't fit the description?''

"Guess?''

Juliet laughed. "Well, as you came here with Mr. Weston I suppose Paul Forbes must be the one out of favor?''

"He's never been *in* favor as far as I'm concerned,'' Stacy declared vehemently.

By this time Juliet had changed out of her costume and into her jeans and sun top. She sat down opposite Stacy. "You were with him last night.''

"The biggest mistake I ever made in my life.'' Remembering his threats of a few minutes ago she thought it just had to be. "For a few brief, *stupid* minutes I thought I may have made a mistake about how awful he is.'' She grimaced. "I hadn't.''

"So, where were you last night?''

Stacy blushed. "I don't know how to tell you that without giving you the wrong impression of what actually happened.''

"I'm not here to pass judgment on anything you did.''

She grinned. "Goodness knows I haven't lived a life of complete innocence."

Stacy couldn't meet her eyes. "I stayed in Jake Weston's suite." She went on to tell Juliet of the event of the night before.

There were bright spots of angry color in Juliet's cheeks by the time Stacy had finished. "Good for Mr. Weston. I hope he hurt Forbes."

"He did."

"Good," she said with satisfaction. "I just hope I see Matthew before you do, though. I don't think he'll hold back long enough to hear what really happened."

"You see what I mean about his brotherly protection."

Juliet nodded. "I'm beginning to. He wasn't exactly jealous, just angry."

Stacy stood up. "So will Jake be if I don't soon make an appearance. Oh, by the way," she said as an afterthought, "he isn't married."

Juliet shrugged. "I told you I could be wrong."

She would never know how glad she was that she had been! "I'd better get out there or he'll think I've been attacked again."

"Are you going to introduce me? I'd love to meet him."

"Come on, then." Stacy chuckled. "Although don't blame me if he snaps your head off. He alternates between being tauntingly flirtatious to cuttingly sarcastic."

"Let's hope I catch him at a good moment. I'd quite like to be flirted with by him."

It appeared they had caught him at the right moment, because within seconds of being introduced to her Jake had Juliet giggling coyly at some of his remarks. Stacy felt herself bridling with unreasonable jealousy.

"We can give you a lift back to the hotel if you don't mind squashing in the back," Jake offered Juliet.

"Don't you have to stay here?" Stacy asked him curtly.

His deep blue eyes flickered over her mockingly. "Not if it means I have to be deprived of the company of *two* beautiful women."

Her mouth pursed angrily as he smiled at Juliet. "In that case I'll sit in the back. I'm sure you and Juliet must still have plenty to talk about."

"That's fine by me," he agreed easily. "If you're sure you'll be comfortable...."

"I'll be fine," she snapped waspishly.

"Right. I'll just go and make my excuses to Payne."

"We'll wait for you by the car." Her manner was off-hand.

"Ooh," breathed Juliet excitedly as they walked side by side to Jake's car. "He's even more fascinating than he looks—if that's possible."

"It's possible."

"Why so grouchy? I think he's absolutely charming. And I love that deep sexy drawl of his."

Stacy clambered into the back of the car, uncaring of the upholstery. "It isn't always deep and sexy," she muttered.

Juliet looked at her closely. "Are you jealous, by any chance?"

She blushed. "No, of course I'm not."

Juliet grinned. "Yes, you are. Hey, come on, he was only being polite. He didn't mean anything by it."

"I don't care if he did," she said crossly. "He has a perfect right to flirt with whom he pleases."

"But you don't like it," her friend climbed into the passenger seat. "Could it be that you've really fallen for our renowned author?"

Stacy colored deeply. "No—"

"Liar!" Juliet contradicted softly.

"Well.... I could have."

"I wouldn't blame you if you have." Juliet settled more comfortably in the seat. "I could fall for him myself if I didn't find Matthew quite so interesting at the moment. He actually got around to kissing me good-night last night," she revealed triumphantly.

"Well, that's a move in the right direction." Stacy was glad to be onto a subject that didn't involve quite so much soul-searching on her part. She *had* fallen for Jake Weston, for all the good it would do her, and she didn't want everyone to know of her stupidity.

Juliet smiled her satisfaction. "That's what I thought. Oh, boy," she sighed. "Here comes Mr. Weston again." Her eyes lighted up with pleasure.

Stacy turned to watch Jake walk toward them with long easy strides, his black silk shirt unbuttoned almost to his waist in the heat of the day to reveal a fine matt of dark silky hair, his muscles rippling as he moved. Stacy felt her pulse race at the sight of him and looked hurriedly away before he could see her interest.

He grinned at them as he got into the driver's seat. "Sorry if I ruined your work for today." He spoke to Juliet, accelerating the car to high speed. "I don't think Paul's in any condition to work today."

She laughed. "So Stacy has been telling me."

Jake glanced fleetingly at Stacy as she sat in the back, the wind blowing through her long hair. "I hope you weren't too worried by Stacy's absence last night?"

Stacy sat behind them glowering angrily as they talked first on one subject and then another. She felt excluded and jealous, and longed for their arrival back at the hotel.

Jake held the door open for them both to get out. "Would you like to join us for lunch?" he asked Juliet.

"I would love to, but I have to look for someone."

He nodded. "Then perhaps we'll see you later."

Stacy was really annoyed by the time he deigned to notice
her presence, snatching her arm out of his grasp as he led
the way over to the hotel entrance. "I don't remember saying I would have lunch with you," she said once Juliet had
left them.

"You didn't," he acknowledged.

"Then why—"

"But you will," he continued as if she hadn't spoken.
"And while we're eating you can tell me what it was you
were talking to Forbes about for so long."

She looked at him uncertainly. "You saw me talking to
him?" She hadn't been aware of him looking at her.

"I see everything you do," he said grimly. He looked
down at her with cold eyes. "You didn't look as if you exactly hated talking to him."

"Looks can be deceptive," she muttered, remembering
her loathing and fear of the other man as he had issued his
threat to her.

"What did he want?" Jake demanded.

"He—"

"And I want the truth, Stacy," he added harshly.

Somehow the truth was too humiliating, having to reveal
Paul Forbes's threat to tell Jake she had enjoyed his rough
treatment of her. "He was just being his nasty self," she
evaded.

"That doesn't answer my question," his mouth was
tight.

She shrugged. "He was just throwing out vindictive
threats."

Jake's eyes narrowed. "What sort of threats?"

"They were just stupid—"

"Tell me, Stacy!" he ordered angrily.

"He said he would get you back for hitting him, that you
wouldn't get away with it."

"I see. And did he happen to mention what form this revenge would take?"

"No," she lied. She just couldn't bring herself to tell Jake of the awful things that awful man had said to her, of his threat to tell Jake that she had already slept with him.

"Are you sure?" Jake's piercing blue eyes probed her pale face.

She attempted a light laugh that didn't quite come off. "He was just venting his anger at being thwarted. He'll get over it." She was sure that he would do no such thing.

"Men like Forbes don't get over anything. Didn't his effort to get you sacked prove that, even without his behavior of last night."

"I suppose so," she admitted. "But I don't have much more to do in the film. A lot of my scenes have already been shot. Another week should be it, and then I can get back to London."

"Do you have any other work lined up?"

She shook her head. "Not for a few weeks, anyway."

"Then there's no reason why you can't stay on here once your work is finished."

"There's a very good one. At the moment my expenses are being paid for me. I certainly couldn't afford to stay here if they weren't. Back in London I share an apartment with three other girls; I've had to keep paying my rent even though I'm not there."

"I could pay your expenses."

She gave him a sharp look. "Just what are you suggesting?"

"The filming will go on for a few weeks after you've left, and I've already missed several weeks. I can't leave after only being here a week."

"I realize that." She frowned.

"I don't want you to go back to London where I can't see you."

"You...you want to see me?"

He gave her a taunting look. "What do you think?" he mocked.

"I have no idea."

"Not even after this morning?" he probed softly.

Bright color flamed in her cheeks. "This morning was, well, it was a result of an accumulation of circumstances."

"The main one being that I want you," he said dryly.

"Yes," she acknowledged huskily.

"It frightens you that I'm so honest, doesn't it?" he mused. "Would you rather I said something like, I fell in love with your screen test, that I was glad I was no longer a married man because I wanted to be free to marry you if you turned out to be as beautiful and enchanting as you looked on film? Would you prefer me to say something like that?"

Stacy smiled. "No. And stop teasing me."

"I'm not teasing you," he said abruptly. "You have to admit it could be true; all the facts fit."

"You're an expert when it comes to fitting fiction to fact."

"But you must admit it would make an interesting story; the hardened cynic falling for a girl half his age, falling so badly he couldn't wait to find out if his feelings were returned. If I were a romantic I'd write the story myself."

"But you aren't, and that's why the story couldn't be true about us. You see women not as people to love but as things to desire, to *want*. That's the only word you've ever used to me, *want*."

"I just offered to tell you I had fallen in love with your screen—"

"Do you have to mock everything?" she interrupted bitterly. "I happen to believe in love."

"And you don't think I would be sincere about falling in love with you?"

She took a deep breath, wishing it could be true and knowing it wasn't. "I believe that, like all men, you would tell a woman what she wanted to hear in order to get what *you* want."

He gave a short laugh. "You're more cynical than you realize, Stacy."

"I'm practical," she corrected. "As the result of a situation very similar to this, I don't welcome the same fate for my child."

"Why didn't your parents marry?"

"Because they didn't love each other. What they had was a purely sexual attraction."

"How do you know that if you were abandoned so young?"

"Because my mother told me," she said angrily. "My mother married a few years after I was born and apparently it was the appearance of the first child of that marriage that finally jogged her conscience into making her go in search of the week-old baby she had abandoned. She found me still at the children's home she left me at, let me know who she was, and then found out that her husband wouldn't even have my name mentioned in the house."

"God, that's crueler than knowing nothing at all."

"Oh, I don't know. At least I had someone. Most of the children there had no one."

"Yes, but to know you had a mother who couldn't even take you home."

"And didn't want to, not if it meant losing what she had," she told him dully. "Do you have any children?"

"Me? No." He appeared shaken by her question.

"Well, don't look so surprised. You have been married."

"There are no children," Jake said harshly.

"There's no need to bite my head off. It could have been a possibility."

"I'll tell you about my marriage some time."

She wished he would tell her about it now. She wanted to know all about this woman he had loved enough to marry, wanted to know what she had to make him want her for his wife. "I'd like that," she told him huskily.

"And in the meantime you'll stay on here?"

"I wasn't angling when I said I couldn't afford to stay," she snapped.

He sighed. "I know that. Will you stay?"

"No. If I did that I would become what everyone already thinks I am."

"And that is?"

"Your mistress," she supplied. "Your kept woman."

"But you'll know you aren't."

"I'll know and you'll know, but I don't see why I should add to gossip by giving anyone the satisfaction of knowing I'm being kept by you. I couldn't do it, anyway. Much as I like this hotel, I would simply be here to amuse you, your plaything. I don't like being under obligation to anyone."

"Too much independence," he said impatiently.

"I've learned over the years only to depend on myself. You stand less chance of being let down that way."

"I think I'd better get you in to lunch; you're getting maudlin. After we've eaten I have to return to the location site. I've taken enough time off for one day. But we can meet for dinner later. Perhaps you would like to go somewhere different to eat, away from all the curious eyes?"

And Paul Forbes! She would welcome that. "That would be nice," she agreed eagerly.

They parted after lunch, Stacy going up to her room and Jake back to work. She found a letter propped up on the dressing table from Juliet, informing her that she was by the pool.

Stacy was undecided about joining her. Matthew was bound to be with her and she wasn't sure of his reaction to seeing her again. After the brief attraction they had had for each other, Matthew had become the nearest thing to a brother she had ever had, and he would not be very pleased with her for making him sit up half the night on her account.

But he had to be faced, and by the pool was perhaps the best place for that. He would be relaxed and not so likely to make a scene.

Her two friends were on loungers beside the bue water when she came down, the remains of a buffet lunch on the table between them. She sat down on a third lounger, looking at Matthew uncertainly.

"You were right about the four pairs of hands," she told him lightly, rubbing oil onto her bikini-clad body.

"So I gathered," he said distantly.

"Matthew?" She looked at him pleadingly.

"What do you want me to say?" He sat up angrily. "You look a mess—your face, your arms—just a complete mess. And all because you wouldn't listen to reason."

"You're right, of course, Matthew."

"And don't think you can get by me by acting all contrite. It's time you realized just how dangerous your impetuous behavior can be."

"I think she knows that already," Juliet put in dryly.

"About damn time, too," he snapped. "Perhaps it's as well it happened; at least it brought you down to earth a bit."

"Matthew!" Juliet said reproachfully. "Leave the poor girl alone."

"Poor girl!" he scoffed. "That's the last thing she is. Spending the night in Jake Weston's suite!"

Stacy gave him a sideways glance. "I believe you spent the best part of the night in our room alone with Juliet," she said, tongue in cheek.

Matthew flushed. "That was different! I—"

"She has a point," Juliet put in mischievously.

"You know damn well it was perfectly innocent," he snapped.

"And how do you know Stacy's night with Mr. Weston wasn't equally as innocent?"

"Well...because it can't have been," he said crossly. "He isn't the sort of man to simply, well, he wouldn't just leave Stacy to—"

Juliet laughed. "For goodness' sake say it, Matthew. You believe Stacy and Mr. Weston to have shared the same bed— and not just to sleep in."

"That's right," he muttered.

"And how does she know we didn't do exactly the same thing?"

"Because you know we didn't."

"I know you *say* you didn't." Stacy joined in Juliet's teasing. "But I only have your word for that—as you only have mine."

Matthew looked at the two of them as they struggled to hold back their humor. "All right, all right," he sighed. "I admit I could be wrong."

"You are wrong," Juliet insisted.

"All right," he conceded with a further sigh. "I am wrong. But you have to agree with me about Stacy's impetuosity."

"She's a big girl, Matthew, and even if she had spent the night in bed with Jake Weston it's none of your business."

"But—"

"Is it, Matthew?" Juliet persisted.

"No!" He stood up. "I'm going for a swim."

Juliet quirked an eyebrow. "To cool off?"

Stacy chuckled at the furious look Matthew directed at them both before diving into the cool water. "You shouldn't tease him like that," she scolded her roommate.

"Then he shouldn't be so bossy and disapproving," Juliet replied unconcernedly.

"Thanks for helping me over that, anyway. I appreciate it."

"That's okay," her friend dismissed. "He really mauled you, didn't he?" She indicated the livid bruises on Stacy's arms.

Stacy grimaced as she remembered the way Paul Forbes had touched her. "Yes."

"I've almost finished my work here," Juliet said with a sigh. "I'll be quite sorry to leave. It's been quite interesting, especially the last few days."

"If you're talking about me, then don't be upset. I'm going back to London myself in a couple of days. We've shot all my scenes but the rape one. Martin Payne seems to be avoiding shooting it, although I have to admit I'm not too eager to do it myself. But I would like to get away. Things have become very complicated around here lately." Not least of all her feelings for Jake.

"You surely don't want to leave Mr. Weston?" Juliet sounded scandalized. "I'd hold onto him for as long as I could."

So would Stacy if she had the chance. But she had meant it when she had told him she didn't go in for affairs, and no matter how tempted she was to stay on here as his guest, she knew she wouldn't do it, couldn't do it.

"I'm only a fleeting attraction for him," she told Juliet. "Once I've left he'll probably take out one of the other girls."

"And just about all of them would be willing to do that."

Stacy turned away so that Juliet couldn't see how much that would hurt her. "I'm sure they would," she agreed softly. "Are you coming in for a swim? I think Matthew should have cooled off by now."

The water was pleasantly warm, and after spending half an hour or so swimming they all got out to dry off in the sun. The conversation didn't return to the subject of Jake Weston or Paul Forbes, something for which Stacy felt grateful. As far as Jake was concerned, Stacy was living from meeting to meeting, and if his only reasons for seeing her were to protect her from Paul Forbes and because he himself desired her, then that was better than nothing. He would demand nothing of her she didn't want to give—he had already said he liked his women willing.

Juliet left them around four, wanting to lay down in the cool room and rid herself of a headache so that she could join Matthew later. But even so Matthew refrained from asking Stacy any more questions, although he did offer to drive her back to London when her work here was finished. "I have more to do myself," he said. "But I told Juliet I would drive her back when she was ready, and so I might as well take both of you."

They were just entering the hotel to go up to their rooms to bathe before dinner, and Stacy reached up to kiss his cheek gratefully. "You're a real friend, Matthew." She smiled.

She turned, the smile still on her face, to find Jake and his lawyer just entering the hotel, the grim look on Jake's face telling her that he had witnessed the kiss she had inno- cently given Matthew. And he looked furious about it!

CHAPTER EIGHT

STACY DRESSED FOR DINNER, not knowing whether Jake would keep their date or not. After a curt nod to the two of them he had marched off in the direction of the bar, and after a resigned shrug Brad Delmain had followed him.

She had made a hurried goodbye to Matthew and rushed to her room before she broke down and cried in front of him. Juliet was asleep and so she quietly went into the bathroom, the sound of the running shower drowning out her crying.

Jake had looked so angry, his hands clenched into fists at his sides, a white tenseness around his mouth. And she had to admit he had good reason. He didn't realize she regarded Matthew as purely a friend, and he had already acted jealous of the younger man. What would he think of her now!

Juliet woke up feeling groggy, but determined to go out with Matthew if it killed her. She had looked better after showering and applying her makeup and had gone off quite happily with Matthew fifteen minutes earlier, leaving Stacy to wait for Jake.

She had dressed with great care, wanting to look her best for him if he did turn up. The skirt of her black gown flowed to just below her knees in fixed pleats, the two tiny cups that made up the bodice held up by two thin straps from the center of her breasts and secured around her neck. The gown gave the impression of being halter-necked, although it was mainly held in place by her uptilted breasts.

Her shoulders were bare and tanned a golden brown.

For once she had secured her hair in a tight knot on top of her head, several loose tendrils alleviating the severity of the style, the black artificial rose pinned to one side of the knot.

She looked what she didn't feel, sophisticated and self-assured. Her makeup was perfect if heavier than she usually wore, the bruises on her arms expertly covered by a light dusting of makeup.

She jumped nervously at the sharp knock on the door, self-consciously checking her appearance in the full-length mirror before opening the door. Her eyes widened at Jake's suave appearance, the white suit and black silk shirt fitting him perfectly, emphasizing the width and power of his shoulders, tapering down to his slim waist and muscular thighs.

He didn't say a word, looking down at her with those cold blue eyes that sent a chill down her spine. She licked her lips nervously. "Good evening," she greeted huskily.

The coldness in his eyes increased. "Is it?" he asked curtly.

She swallowed hard. "I—I thought so."

"Did you indeed?" he snapped.

"Yes," she said miserably.

"Well, are you going to ask me in or do you have Day in there?"

She gasped. "Matthew? But Matthew is—"

"I have no wish to hear what he is or isn't." He pushed the door open, walking past her into the room. "Come here," he ordered, his eyes narowed. Stacy watched him with wide frightened eyes, holding onto the door for support. She had expected him to perhaps be angry, but he was in such a cold rage he wasn't even asking for an explanation, condemning her unheard. She shook her head in answer to his command.

Jake came toward her with controlled violence, wrenching the door out of her hand and slamming it noisily before pulling her roughly into his arms and taking fierce possession of her lips.

Stacy felt her knees buckle at the violence behind his kiss, trembling with uncontrolled fear at the determination behind his plundering of her mouth.

"Kiss me, damn you," he muttered through gritted teeth. "Show me some of that passion every other man seems to get from you."

Twice in as many days she had been physically attacked, and yet with this man she found not revulsion but the stirring of pleasure, feeling herself weakening toward him as his mouth claimed hers once more.

Jake held her head immovable as he deepened the kiss, bending her back over his arm so that she couldn't move away from him without falling over. Not that she really wanted to move away from him, kissing him back now as she smoothed the dark thickness of his hair at his nape.

"That's better," he murmured against her throat, pulling her down into the armchair so that she lay across him. His lips burned a trail across her throat, her shoulders, and down to the hollow between her breasts.

Stacy gasped as she felt him pulling the pins out of her hair. "What are you doing?"

He wound the long red tresses around her throat. "I'm debating whether to strangle you right now or wait until after I've made love to you."

She pushed against him but was firmly wedged against him in the confines of the chair. "But you... you can't," she pleaded.

He tightened the pressure of her hair. "It would be so easy, and I would enjoy it."

"I meant you can't make love to me."

His taunting blue eyes ran insolently over her defenceless body. "I can't, can't I? There's a bed over there, you're in my arms, and I think you owe it to me."

"I *owe* it to you? Why you—"

He stilled her struggle. "*Yes*, you owe it to me!" he said savagely. "I've stood back while you've flirted with Day and Forbes, given them the pleasure you deny me, and I'm not going to stand back and watch any longer. You're very deceptive on film, Stacy. I felt sure you were as innocent as you look. And yet you're constantly with one man or another."

"No, Jake, that isn't true. Matthew—"

"I don't want to hear about your other men," he snapped, standing up with her held firmly in his arms. "Tonight I'm going to be the only man on your mind. Going on the amount of men you have interested in you here alone, I would say that innocent look of yours hides an experience that could prove very entertaining."

"No!" She fought against him as he lowered her onto the bed before discarding his jacket to join her. And she had thought he would never force her into a relationship she didn't want. Right now he was beyond reason! "No, please, I don't—"

"Shut up, Stacy," he rasped. "I have no idea what you thought you would get if you held out against me, but I'm afraid I'm past being convinced now. I left you alone for a few hours this afternoon and you were off with Day. So now that I know you for what you are, you can forget trying to dupe me. I'll buy you all the usual trinkets, but please, no more pretending."

Stacy was speechless. He truly believed her to have been playing a part, and he was set on making love to her right now!

He smoothed her hair back from her face, his lips trailing

across her eyes and cheeks. "You're very young to have become so promiscuous." He shrugged. "But who am I to judge the way you choose to live. I just want you—and *now*," he said urgently.

His mouth was seductive now, playing with her senses as his hands ran caressingly over her body. Her eyes closed as she felt him release the two thin straps that secured her gown, trembling as his long tapered fingers touched her breasts, bringing them to full pulsating life.

"Jake, I...." She gasped her pleasure. "Please be gentle," she pleaded.

"Don't worry, I realize you don't like rough handling. Your reaction to Forbes showed me that," he murmured, his head bent as his mouth probed her sensitive skin.

That wasn't what she meant at all. She could see no way of stopping him from taking what he wanted from her, and if he had to take her then she wanted him to be gentle. If she had to become someone's mistress it might as well be the man she was in love with.

She fought for sanity as his mouth teased and caressed her breasts, knowing she had to tell him the truth about herself before he went any further, had to tell him of her complete inexperience. "Jake, I—"

"I don't want to talk." He claimed her mouth once again.

Stacy was feeling dizzy by the time his attention returned to her hardened nipples. "Please, you have to listen," she begged. "If you have to do this to me, then at least know you'll be the first."

He became very still beside her, drawing a ragged breath, finally lifting his head to search her feverish features for the sincerity of her words. Finally he shook his head. "I don't believe you. Nothing you can say can stop me now. You may not be what I first expected, but I'm still determined to have you."

She lay limply in his arms. "I'm not trying to stop you," she said dully. "You'll know the truth soon enough."

His eyes narrowed as he looked down at her. "You have to be lying."

"Why do I? Just because you've seen me with Matthew a couple of times and Paul Forbes tried to rape me doesn't mean I—"

"You lived with Day," he accused. "You told me that yourself."

"I didn't *live* with him, he moved in with me for a while."

"A sort of trial marriage that didn't work out," he taunted.

"Nothing of the sort," she denied.

"Oh, I see," he said sarcastically. "Neither of you made any pretense that marriage was what you had in mind."

He moved his body from over her, and she began to regain some of her composure, although his closeness on the bed was still unnerving. "You're deliberately misunderstanding me," she rebuked. "All the time Matthew stayed at my apartment he slept on the sofa."

"Is that true?"

"Yes."

"Bloody idiot," he muttered.

"He had nowhere else to stay or he wouldn't have been there at all."

"Am I expected to believe all this?"

She sighed. "Believe what you want. But please believe me when I say you'll be the first."

He lay back at her side. "You have to be lying." He looked at her, briefly touching her naked breasts. "Your body is beautiful. Many men must have lost themselves in that beauty." He sat up to shake her. "You have to be lying. Stacy, tell me you're lying!"

"I can't." She blinked back her tears.

"So you're a tease, is that it?" he demanded grimly.

"I can't." She blinked back her tears.

"So you're a tease, is that it?" he demanded grimly. "You push a man to the edge and then dare him to take your virginity. Is that the way it happened with Forbes? Did he have trouble regaining control?"

"No! No, Jake, that isn't what happened. I'm not trying to stop you, am I?"

He gave a harsh laugh. "In the most effective way possible. You're daring me to take you, and if by some mischance I did happen to be your first lover, I'd feel as guilty as hell." He stood up, buttoning his shirt. "I take back my offer of protection. After today I think it's the men who need protection from you. For someone so young you've learned how to torture a man in the cruelest way possible." He shrugged his broad shoulders into his jacket.

Stacy secured her gown with shaking fingers. "You...you aren't leaving?"

"Yes, I'm leaving. Before I pass the stage of not caring a damn whether you're telling the truth or not."

Her bottom lip trembled. "Oh, Jake, please don't go like this. I'm none of the things you think me. I just happen to lo—" She broke off as she realized the enormity of her declaration. She couldn't just baldly state that she loved him; he wouldn't believe her anyway.

"Yes?" he queried sharply.

"Nothing," she evaded his eyes.

"Let me finish for you," he said bitterly. "You just happen to loathe all men."

"No! That isn't true." She shook her head dazedly.

"I think you'll find that it is. And you enjoy the power your beauty gives over all of us. Well, not me, lady," he said harshly. "I don't plead with any woman for her body. As far as I'm concerned one woman's body is as good as another. And I don't want any part of your emotional hang-ups. You would be doing us both a favor if you stayed out of my way in future," he warned. His American accent was much more noticeable in his anger.

"I'll be leaving for London soon," she said miserably.

"Day driving you?"

She sighed. "Yes."

"All I can say is that he's a glutton for punishment. Do you go back to him after all your affairs?" he sneered.

Stacy struck out at him without thinking, her finger marks and scratches from her nails standing out lividly against his white angry face. She stepped back in horror at what she had done. "I—Oh, God, I'm sorry," she said brokenly.

"Don't apologize." Cold disdain entered his voice. "Good night."

"Don't you mean goodbye?" she halted him at the door.

"I'm not sure," he snapped. "I'll let you know."

"Wh—what do you mean?" she asked tremulously.

He shrugged. "I may decide to risk your challenge—if nothing better comes along, of course. There are some beautiful women here that I could quite—"

"Get out, Jake!" she cut in, her voice shaking. "Go and find one of these women. I'm sure most of them will be obliging."

"So am I," he taunted.

"Go away. I'm glad I hit you!" she added defiantly.

"You may not be if I should decide to take up your challenge." He ran his fingers over what must surely have been very painful and must sting even now. "Because if I do, the first thing I'll do is make you pay for this."

"You won't get the chance."

His mocking laughter could still be heard as he walked off down the corridor. So it hadn't taken Paul Forbes to ruin things between herself and Jake—she seemed to have managed that very well on her own.

She felt numb as she prepared herself for bed, knowing that she couldn't face anyone now, and her appetite had completely deserted her anyway. Jake had come to her room tonight with one intention and one intention only. And he might have succeeded, too, if she hadn't told him that she had had no other lovers.

Juliet had left for her final day's filming when Stacy awoke from her drugging sleep, and Stacy felt reluctant to move. One more day and she could be away from this mess, but it was a day she dreaded.

She had agreed to do this rape scene with Paul Forbes only on one condition, that there would be no nudity on her part. But even so it was going to be an embarrassing part of the film for her.

It was very late by the time she came downstairs for her breakfast, so late that there was only one other person present as she entered the dining room. Brad Delmain, Jake's lawyer.

He looked up and smiled at her as she hesitated about going to a table. As she knew him it would look very rude for her to sit apart from him, and yet she didn't really want to get into conversation with him. He was sure to say something about Jake, and she didn't want to talk about him.

"Come and join me," he invited, as she had known he would.

"But you've nearly finished," she pointed out shyly.

"I have finished," he confirmed. "I'm merely lingering over my coffee to waste time. I'd much rather use that time talking to you."

She really had no other choice than to join him, ordering toast and coffee for herself. "Why are you wasting time?"

"I have a flight back to the States today. My business here is finished."

She rested her chin on her hands as she leaned forward onto the table. "I didn't realize you were here to work."

Brad gave a smile. "Aren't we all?"

She gave a light laugh. "I suppose so."

"You've argued with Jake, haven't you?" he stated bluntly.

She almost dropped the knife she was using to butter her toast. "I— What makes you think that?"

He laughed at her evasion. "I don't think it, Stacy, I know it. You left your mark on him for everyone to see."

She blushed at his forthright manner. "Oh."

"He probably deserved it," he continued. "Jake tends to act first and think later."

As far as she was concerned that hadn't been the case last night. Jake's actions had all been premeditated, very carefully thought out. He had had one thought on his mind, and that had been to make love to her.

"You don't agree with me." Brad was watching her closely. "Perhaps you've come to know a different side of him."

"Perhaps, I'm not sure. Jake seems to live by one set of rules and expects everyone else to live by another one."

He looked interested. "Am I allowed to ask what you mean by that?"

"Jake has, well, he has women in his life. No, please," she pleaded at his humor. "I'm trying to tell you. He has women, but he objects to the same women being involved with several men."

"Meaning you?"

"Not necessarily." She didn't want this conversation to become too personal to herself.

He pursed his lips. "What do you know of Jake's personal life?" he asked slowly.

She shrugged. "After last night I don't think I know anything about him at all, let alone his personal life. He's an enigma, totally incomprehensible."

"He isn't normally."

Her eyes widened. "Are you saying I've made him like that?"

"It would appear so. I've never seen him like this before. When he left you last night he went back to his suite and got stoned out of his mind. He was asleep in the chair when I went in to see him this morning. And he wasn't in a good mood to answer any of my questions. Needless to say your finger marks still showed on his face."

"How did you know it was me?" she asked curiously

"I tried mentioning your name and got my head bitten off. But let's get back to why Jake is like he is. He's had several women, in his life, not nearly as many as you think, but there have been women. And you know he was married."

"Yes." She sipped her coffee. "I'm not really sure we should be talking about him like this."

"I think I have to try and explain his attitude to you. Jake has been a good friend of mine for years now. I've seen him triumphant and I've seen him in the depths of despair, and I don't think that what I'm about to tell you can harm him in any way. He was married for twenty years to a woman who should never have been any man's wife."

Stacy swallowed hard, her face pale. "Twenty years?" she repeated dully. It was a lifetime! She had thought perhaps he had been married a couple of years and it hadn't worked out, but *twenty years*!

Brad nodded. "It's a long time if you take it at its face value. In actual fact Jake and Margaret only lived together for a year of that time, the year it took Jake to learn she had a sickness no one man could satisfy."

She blushed as his meaning became clear to her. "I don't think Jake would thank you for telling me this."

He smiled. "One day he just might do that," he disagreed. "He's lived alone too long, shut himself away from emotion too long. And I'm not talking about physical emotion," he added as she made to protest. "A man as virile as Jake would need an outlet physically, but that's all it's ever been. Margaret soured him for marriage, I'm afraid."

"I don't think I want to hear any more. This is his private life and—"

"And you love him."

Stacy looked stricken. "No!"

"Please don't attempt to deny it," he said gently. "I've been a lawyer too long not to know when someone is lying to me."

She smiled wanly. "That must be very helpful in your cases."

"It can be frustrating when I know someone is not guilty and yet I know I'm going to lose my case. But we're getting away from the point."

"Yes," she sighed. 'You said that Jake's wife soured him for marriage. If he felt that way why didn't he just divorce her and rid himself of her once and for all?"

"Ordinarily that would have been the thing to do, but there was the child, and—"

"Child?" she queried sharply. "There's a child?"

He nodded. "Yes, a boy."

"But he . . . he told me he doesn't have any children."

"He doesn't—now. Danny died twelve years ago. He was seven."

"Oh, God." She felt faint. "How awful."

"Yes. It wouldn't have been so bad if Margaret hadn't kept blaming herself for it." He took a deep breath. "I'm not explaining this very well. When Jake realized exactly what his wife was he moved out of their house and into an apartment. Unfortunately, unknown to either of them, Margaret was already pregnant with Danny. Over the next five years they tried on and off to make a go of it, but it just didn't work out. And yet Margaret was really good with the boy, an ideal mother in fact. And if Danny had more uncles than any other kid in the neighborhood he didn't seem to realize it.''

"Surely if things were as bad as that, Jake could have taken the boy away from her?''

"Like I said, you couldn't fault her behavior as a mother. So it went on year after year, Jake married and yet not married, the one thing holding them together the love they both felt for the boy. Then Danny died.''

"What happened?''

"He had leukemia. It was as if Danny had been the only thing holding Margaret on the ground; after his death she was either high on booze or drugs the whole time.''

"And Jake?'' she asked quietly, shocked and appalled by the tragic past Jake hid from everyone.

"Jake has his own way of dealing with grief. He works himself until he drops. And drop he did. He was as much of a wreck as Margaret for about a year. He really loved that kid. But finally he came to his senses and set about building what life he could, something Margaret was never able to do.''

"Why did she die?''

"Now that's something you'll have to ask Jake about if you really want to know, and if he really wants to tell you. I'm just trying to explain to you why he hits the roof every time he sees you with another man. He can't take that from a woman after Margaret.''

"But I've tried to explain to him that they mean nothing to me.''

Brad shook his head. "That wouldn't mean a thing to him. Do you think Margaret didn't tell him the same thing time and time again. The only trouble with her was that they *didn't* mean a thing, she just needed them like she needed oxygen."

"Poor Jake."

"Indeed," he agreed. "I just hope what I've told you has helped you to understand him a little better."

"Understand him, yes. But I still don't see why he should get so upset about me seeing my friends. We hardly know one another well enough for him to act so possessively."

"You've known him long enough to fall in love with him, and Jake—well, you'll have to ask him about his feelings for you."

She turned away. "I already know his feelings. He made them very clear last night."

He chuckled. "I seem to remember you made certain feelings clear last night, too, but they aren't your true ones."

"That's different. I—"

"Not at all," he rebuked. "You acted out of anger. He did the same thing and yet you're condemning him for it. The next time he sees you he'll probably apologize."

"I wouldn't count on it," she said wryly.

"Neither would I if he hasn't calmed down. He had a hell of a hangover this morning. Ready to leave?" he indicated her empty coffee cup.

Stacy sighed. "I suppose so." She was so confused with what this man had told her about Jake.

They left the dining room together, Stacy unsure of how she was going to spend the rest of the day. If she went down to the film set she would undoubtedly see Jake, and yet she didn't want to stay here at the hotel on her own.

"Speak of the devil," Brad muttered at her side, keeping

a firm hold of her arm as she would have moved away.

Jake had entered the hotel and was now making his way toward them, his face grim. His blue eyes flickered scathingly over the hold Brad had of her arm and Stacy felt herself tensing for his sarcasm.

"Give him a chance," Brad murmured for her ears alone.

"To do what?" she muttered back. "He looks murderous."

Brad chuckled. "He wouldn't get violent here in front of everyone."

"I wouldn't count on it."

Jake had reached them by now and after a contemptuous look in her direction he turned to his friend. "I came to say goodbye and apologize for my churlish behavior this morning. I didn't realize you would have company."

"Stacy and I had breakfast together."

Jake's speculative look seemed to ask what else they had done together. "You're leaving now?"

"In a few minutes," Brad confirmed.

Blue eyes turned to focus on Stacy again and she saw the reason Brad had known she had hit him. On the left side of his face there were three scratch marks on his cheek where she must have caught him with her nails.

"Is there something wrong?" Jake asked her coldly as she continued to stare at him.

She looked hurriedly away. "No, nothing," she mumbled.

"Good." He turned back to Brad. "You'll check on that business for me when you get back?"

"Yes." He looked at his watch. "Actually, I have to be off now. Thank you for keeping me company, Stacy. And remember what I told you."

"I'll remember," she said quietly.

There was a stilted silence between them once Brad had left, she nervous and shy with him, and Jake withdrawn and haughty.

He, too, looked at his wristwatch. "I'll have to be getting back," he said tersely.

Stacy tentatively touched his arm. "I, er, I'm sorry about your face."

"Don't be," he snapped. "In your estimation I probably deserved it. I didn't realize you were that friendly with Brad."

She frowned. "*That* friendly?"

He shrugged. "I suppose I should have guessed, really. He's a man, isn't he?"

"Just what do you mean by that?"

"Every man who looks at you wants you," he remarked coldly. "Brad was attracted to you from the start. And you like a man's adoration."

"No! That isn't true, Jake. Brad—"

He shook off her hand. "I don't want to know."

"But I'm not like that. I'm not like Marg—" She broke off, biting her top lip painfully.

His fingers dug into her arms as he restrained her. "Like who?" he demanded, his eyes narrowed in glittering anger.

She couldn't meet that look. "I'm just not like that. I— Let me go, Jake. You're hurting me."

"I'd like to do more than that," he ground out savagely. "What do you know about Margaret?"

"Who?" she evaded.

He gave a cruel bitter laugh. "It's too late for prevarication. Now tell me," he shook her. "What do you know about my wife?"

"Nothing." She struggled against him. "I don't know anything."

"It was Brad, damn him," he snapped. "You've been

having a cozy little chat with him about me and my sex-crazed alcoholic wife."

"No—"

"Oh, yes," he insisted. "You have a way of making men talk to you. But he had no right to tell you anything about my marriage."

"He did it for the best," she explained pleadingly. "He thought it would help—"

"Help what?" he bit out coldly. "We know all we need to know about each other, and what I've come to know about you I don't like." He pushed her roughly away from him as if she burned him. "Did you see the similarity between yourself and my wife?" he taunted.

Stacy's face went white with shock. "No! You're wrong," she choked. "She was ill. She—"

His mouth turned back in a sneer. "And what do you call your affairs—a healthy appetite?" he scorned. "I can think of a better name for it."

"Jake, please—"

"Oh, get out of my sight," he said fiercely, marching away from her with long angry strides.

CHAPTER NINE

EVERYONE WAS STANDING around the film location. A brief storm had made the rape scene in the cove impossible to film this morning, and although it had cleared up now it was still overcast.

These were the times Stacy hated the most, just sitting around waiting for the right weather. And it would have to be today of all days, the day she had been dreading for the last few weeks, and even more so since Paul Forbes's attack on her.

He came to stand beside her now. "Looking forward to it?" he taunted.

She stopped chewing her lip long enough to glare at him. "Like an appendectomy."

He gave a cruel laugh. "That's a shame, because I'm going to enjoy every minute of it."

"You disgust me!"

"I know." He was still laughing as he walked away.

Damn him! She hated him more than she had ever hated anyone in her life before, and once she had got this scene over she hoped she never had to see him ever again.

"What did he want?" Juliet had come down to keep her company even though she had officially finished her work.

Stacy grimaced. "What do you think?"

"I suppose he was being his usual obnoxious self."

"He can't be anything else."

"I think they're getting ready for filming now." She

looked at Stacy's pale face. "They did a good job on your makeup."

Stacy touched her mouth. "It's not too bad now that the swelling has gone down."

"I think they're ready for you now," Juliet said gently.

"Oh, God." Stacy's hand trembled. "Wish me luck," she begged.

"I do," Juliet squeezed her hand encouragingly. "Off you go."

She was supposed to run along the shoreline pursued by five or six of the marauding sailors, their sole task in life to steal as much and rape as many girls as they could. Of course the story was written mainly to appeal to the male population, mainly consisting of exciting sea battles and skirmishes, but like all good stories there had to be some romance. Paul Forbes played the sea captain, the winner of many fair maidens, but wanting only one to the point of desperation.

And she was that one, taken once by force before finally being wooed and married by her roving sea captain. Of course, the way Jake Weston wrote it women had a very small part in the actual story, his main interest being in the actual sailing of the ship and the adventures encountered at sea. More women had been added to the story as a way of appealing to more of the public.

Now Stacy had to flee from them, caught by one but claimed as the prize of the captain. And she was dreading it, especially as Jake was standing with Martin Payne. Everyone who wasn't needed for this shot had been sent back to the hotel, so at least she could be grateful for that. But it was Jake's presence here that actually bothered her the most, his all-seeing eyes narrowed and speculative.

The first part of it went all right, with her running as if in fear of her life, her hair breaking free of its binding, her feet bare in the golden sand. The men fought over her as she fell, the captain finally moving forward to claim her for himself.

This was all shot in one sequence, the camera moving in for her ravishing among the rocks. She set her teeth as Paul Forbes bent over her, her eyes closed to shut out the gleaming sadism in his face.

Of course, both their reactions were ideal for the film, but her fear of this man was so great that she was shaking all over. His mouth on her made her cringe, his hands on her body nauseating her. She struggled to escape him but he had her pinioned beneath him, and she was aware that he was aroused at her dislike of him.

"Fight, you little bitch," he encouraged in a savage whisper in her ear, so softly that it wouldn't be picked up on sound. "Go on, fight me."

"God, you're loathesome," she muttered vehemently.

His teeth gleamed down at her before he bent his head and bit her ear. Her cry of outrage and pain only seemed to incense him more and she felt the front of her dress rip. Her eyes widened with shock and surprise. This wasn't supposed to happen. She had only agreed to do this scene at all because they had assured her there would be no nudity.

She was fighting in earnest now, scratching and clawing at him, the front of her dress in ruins.

Suddenly he was wrenched off her, a fist landing in his face and knocking him to the ground. Jake stood over him, his face a picture of livid anger. "Get off her, you bastard!" His teeth were savagely bared. "You filthy scum!"

Paul Forbes sat on the sand rubbing his jaw. "She was enjoying it, you fool," he scorned. "Her sort always does."

Jake pulled him to his feet by the scruff of his neck. "You make me sick," he ground out. "You're the lowest form of life."

The actor laughed. "She likes a man to be rough with her. I would have thought you would have found that out by now."

Stacy stood up on shaking legs, tears streaming down her face. "You lying—"

Jake turned to her. "It's all right, honey." He pulled off his jacket and wrapped it around her shoulders as she shivered uncontrollably. "Come on," he said gently. "Let's get you out of here."

Martin Payne had joined them by this time, his face flushed. "What on earth is going on here? You can't just interrupt a scene like this, Jake. We were in the middle of filming."

"Talk to me about it later," Jake dismissed.

"But— Where are you going?" he called after them as Jake gently led her away.

"Where the hell do you think?" Jake rasped. "And keep that bastard away from me or I'll kill him with my bare hands."

"But—" Martin Payne was obviously out of his depth. "We haven't finished filming."

"Oh, yes, you have. Use what you've got. Stacy certainly isn't going near him again."

She was huddled against his side, a bundle of misery and embarrassment. Although there weren't many people here, what there were were staring at them with unconcealed curiosity.

"You're a fool, Weston," Paul Forbes called after them mockingly. "She's a better actress than even you realize. Do you really think I didn't take her the other night?" he gave a short laugh. "She enjoyed every minute of it."

Stacy held Jake's arm as he would have turned angrily back on the other man. "He isn't worth it, Jake," she said dully.

"Didn't you hear what he said?" he demanded roughly. "And for everyone to hear."

"What does it matter? It's been said now; nothing you do or say can undo that."

"But he—"

"Listen to her, Weston," Paul Forbes taunted. "She knows I've only told you the truth. And you can't deny the truth."

A numbness had overtaken her now and she turned away without saying another word. Everywhere she looked there seemed to be hostile, accusing faces, people who she knew to be her friends suddenly appearing as enemies.

Juliet came to her side as she stumbled away, helping her up the rocky pathway. "Are you all right?" she asked gently.

"Yes."

Juliet turned to Jake. "She's in shock, Mr. Weston. I think we should get her to a doctor."

"No!" Stacy said forcefully. "No doctor."

Jake was once again the cold removed stranger, his fierce anger seeming like a dream. "Juliet's right, you should see a doctor."

"No!" her voice rose shrilly. "I just want to get away from here. I'm going back to the hotel to pack my things, and I'm leaving here today."

"You're seeing a doctor first," he insisted. "You've had a lot of shocks the last few days."

"Shocks!" she repeated hysterically. "If you mean almost being raped by two men, then I suppose you're right."

"Two men...?" Juliet looked at Jake Weston with dawning comprehension.

"But then you don't think it was only almost, do you, Jake?" she continued bitterly. "You would rather believe that...that.... You would rather believe Paul Forbes's version of what happened. But then that's because you believe me to be a girl who sleeps with who I feel like."

"Stacy!" Juliet was obviously shocked by her outburst. "You really are in shock."

"I'm nothing of the sort," she denied heatedly. "That is what he believes. Go on, ask him," she invited. "Tell her, Jake. Tell her what you think of me."

"If you don't calm down I will be forced to slap you," he said coldly.

"I wouldn't give you that satisfaction. Physical force seems to be the only thing men understand. Quite frankly I'm sick of the lot of you." She felt physically sick that he could actually believe Paul Forbes's story. The actor had certainly had his revenge on her in the best way possible, completely alienating the man she loved.

Juliet looked bemused by her vehemence. "You should be thanking Mr. Weston," she scolded gently. "No one else would have dared to thwart the man. The others would have let him rape you right there in front of them."

Stacy gave a bitter laugh. "Mr. Weston is under the impression I would have preferred that. I like every cheap thrill I can get, didn't you know that?"

"I warned you," Jake said grimly, his hand landing with a resounding slap on her cheek.

"You...you pig!" Tears of pain cascaded down her cheeks. "That's all you understand, isn't it?" she accused. "Sex and brutality."

Jake gave Juliet a grim smile. "I don't think she needs that doctor after all. She seems to be back to her normal self."

"Oh, I—" began Juliet.

"What do you expect when you hit me?" Stacy demanded.

"Surely that just makes us even?" he taunted.

She couldn't believe this was the same man who had leaped to her defense only minutes earlier. She pulled his leather jacket from about her shoulders and threw it at him. "Come on, Juliet," she said stiffly. "Let's get away from here."

Jake grasped her arm and swung her around to face him. "I'm driving you back to the hotel."

Her green eyes sparkled angrily. "Don't bother. We can find our own way."

He ignored her protests, dragging her toward the car. "You'll do as you're damn well told. I've had enough arguments out of you lately. "I'll give you a thorough beating if you don't shut up."

"Sex and brutality!" she muttered as he pushed her into the passenger seat.

"With you it always turns out to be just brutality," he murmured softly against her ear.

"Oh, I know that." She glared at him.

"Behave yourself," he warned. "Or I just might try and carry out the other half of it."

"You might try, but you wouldn't succeed."

"Don't kid yourself," he mocked. "I can take you any time I want."

"Want!" she scorned. "That's all you feel, isn't it, want and desire?"

"With you it's difficult not to. Now behave, you're embarrassing Juliet." He walked around the back of the car to get in behind the wheel.

The drive back was completed in silence, Jake quietly concentrating on his driving, Juliet tactfully holding her tongue, and Stacy quietly seething. As far as she was concerned, the sooner she went back to London the better.

Jake didn't bother to get out of the car as she and Juliet scrambled out onto the forecourt of the hotel. He leaned over to secure the door. "I would see if you can get this little hellcat to lie down for a while." He spoke to Juliet.

"I'll try," she promised shyly.

"I have no intention of lying down," Stacy cut in angrily. "I'm getting the first train out of here."

Jake's eyes narrowed. "You'll be here when I get back tonight," he stated coldly.

"I will not!"

He sighed impatiently. "Try and talk some sense into this child, Juliet. I don't have the time right now... or the patience." He accelerated the car away from the hotel.

The two girls went up to their room, Stacy slamming drawers as she packed her suitcase.

"You really should listen to him, Stacy." Her friend sat on the bed watching her. "He knows what's best."

Stacy threw her costume down on the bed, hating it and anything to do with the film. "If I listened to everything he said I would have been in bed with him that first evening. That was when he first told me he *wanted* me," she explained scathingly. "He doesn't know the meaning of the word love."

"He did help you."

"Oh, yes," she agreed. "But only because he doesn't like shop-soiled goods."

"Paul Forbes was pretty rude about you. And in front of everyone. You should have let Mr. Weston hit him again. I would have."

"Paul Forbes is a liar," Stacy said with a sigh. "And anyone who really knows me would know he was lying. Jake doesn't know me, doesn't *care* to know me."

Juliet grinned. "You don't give him the chance. You snap and snarl at him the whole time. And that isn't the real you."

Stacy slumped down on her own single bed. "I don't snap

and snarl all the time, just since he gained the impression I'm some sort of bed-hopping groupie of the stars. Paul Forbes threatened to tell Jake those lies, but it didn't really matter, he already believed it anyway. You can't fight the inevitable, Juliet, and Jake doesn't have much faith in women." She couldn't tell the other girl of the reasons for this; that would be breaking a confidence. "I just seem to have added to his disillusionment," she added wryly.

"But only through misunderstandings. If you just explained to him—"

"What could be the point?" Stacy cut in resignedly. "Maybe I could explain away the men here, and maybe we would continue to see each other, but what happens the next time he thinks I've looked at another man for too long, smiled too brightly at another man?" She shook her head. "I couldn't live like that, just waiting for the next flare-up of temper."

"But—"

"Leave it, Juliet, please." She shut her suitcase. "I just want to get away from here and anything that reminds me of Jake."

"At least wait until tonight. Matthew is driving us both back then."

"I daren't run the risk of running into Jake again. If he tries to charm me again, I don't think I could resist him."

"You can always have dinner in your room. No one would expect you to face Paul Forbes after his disgraceful behavior today."

"I suppose I could," she agreed slowly, not relishing the thought of getting a train back. "As you say, I have no need to see anyone before I go."

It was just her luck that night that Jake was traveling down in the elevator she had summoned to take her down to the reception area. Instead of her getting into the elevator, Jake got out, taking in the two suitcases in her hands at a glance.

"I was just coming to see you," he told her coldly.

Stacy had angrily pressed the button again for the elevator to come back to her floor, steeling herself not to look at the devastating picture he made in the black evening suit and snowy white shirt, his dark hair brushed rakishly back from his handsome face.

"Really?" She quirked an eyebrow, impatiently tapping her fingers against the elevator panel. "Well, here I am."

"Yes." He leaned in front of her, in her line of vision. "Where do you think you're going?"

"Where does it look like?" she looked pointedly at her suitcases.

"I told you—"

"I couldn't give a damn what you told me!" Her eyes flashed angrily. "I've always done what *I* wanted to do, and nothing that has happened here has changed that." She stepped into the elevator as it arrived back at her floor, not bothering to hold back her resentment as he got in beside her, arrogantly pressing the button for his own floor. "What do you think you're doing?" she demanded. "Matthew and—"

"Matthew can damn well wait for you," he cut in harshly. "You aren't going anywhere until we've sorted this thing out."

Stacy sighed. "There's nothing to sort out. I've thought it all out, Jake, and what you need is a woman you can lock up for the duration of your interest in her. I can understand why you're so suspicious, but I've always thought trust was essential in any relationship. You don't know the meaning of the word." She trailed along behind him as he led the way to his suite, her suitcases in his hands. "Couldn't you just let me go so that we can both forget we ever met? I've never had reason to question my friendship with any man, and I don't intend to let you force me into it. I owe you no explanations."

"Finished?" He handed her one of the two glasses of whiskey he had poured out.

"No." She took a huge gulp of the whiskey, choking as the fiery liquid burned her throat. "No, I haven't finished." She wiped the tears away from her flushed cheeks. "Why can't you just leave things as they are and let me go, find yourself someone else to amuse you."

He gave a brief bitter smile. "You don't amuse me, Stacy. You put me through hell, but you don't amuse me."

"The hell is of your own making, because you choose to listen to what other people say about me rather than what you yourself know to be true. I really think we've said enough to each other the last few days. You aren't good for me, Jake. You take away my pride and my self-respect."

"I—"

"You want me," she finished dully. "I know that. It's this want and desire that keeps bringing you back to me."

"It isn't only want and desire."

"Whatever it is, it isn't enough."

"You prefer Day, I suppose," he bit out angrily.

"You see," she said with a sigh. "You can't rid yourself of the idea that every man I come into contact with has shared my bed."

He took a step toward her. "Perhaps if you allowed me to share your bed I might be able to feel more sure of you."

She shook her head sadly. "You wouldn't, Jake. A physical relationship isn't the answer to everything."

He gave a wry smile. "But it helps," he said mockingly.

"No."

"Stay here with me. Don't leave."

She turned away from the raw hunger in his eyes, her

love for this man making her feel weak. "Matthew is waiting for me downstairs." She was deliberately provocative, not telling him that Juliet was there, too. "I can't keep him waiting any longer."

"Day!" Jake said scathingly, pulling her roughly against the lean length of his body. "Why must you keep pushing the guy down my throat?" His voice was seductively soft.

She arched her eyebrows at him. "Why do you think?"

"I have no idea." He gently lowered his lips to claim hers, exploring her mouth with a thoroughness that left her breathless. "Can you deny that you enjoyed that?"

She trembled against him. "I'm going home with Matthew, Jake." She didn't answer his question.

He broke off kissing her throat, his eyes narrowed. "What does that mean?"

"It means he's taking me home—and he won't return here until tomorrow morning."

He stepped back with barely suppressed violence. "Are you telling me—"

"I'm telling you what you expect to hear," she evaded. "And Matthew doesn't like to be kept waiting."

"So he's the one you really want?"

Stacy nodded. "Goodbye, Jake." She picked up her suitcases and left.

She sat in front of the television watching the serial that appeared twice a week, and although of late she had watched every single one of this particular serial, she hadn't taken any of it in. She had in fact taken little interest in anything the last few months.

She stood up as the doorbell rang, sinking back into her chair as Helen came out of her bedroom and offered to answer it. Stacy didn't mind in the least. Everything was too much of an effort lately, anyway.

"It's for you," Helen called out cheerfully on her way out. "See you later."

Stacy looked up as Juliet and Matthew came into the room, the sparkling diamond on Juliet's finger evidence of their recent engagement. Juliet had at last got her way and made Matthew take her seriously.

At the moment the two of them were dressed rather grandly in preparation of going to the premiere of the film they had all appeared in. Juliet looked rather splendid in a white Grecian gown, and Matthew looked very distinguished in his black evening suit and white shirt.

Matthew looked surprised at Stacy's appearance, her hair tied back from her pale face, her denims creased, her jumper skintight. "Stacy!" He was obviously exasperated. "You aren't ready."

"Probably because I'm not going," she told him calmly. "Please, sit down." She sat down herself, her knees tucked up under her skirt.

Juliet sat down but Matthew remained standing. "What do you mean, you aren't going? You have to go."

"Of course I don't, Matthew. I received my invitation like everyone else, but I don't have to attend."

"I don't understand you," he said angrily. "You've been moping around like this for months now. The only time you go out is to work—and if you continue to let yourself go like this there won't be any work available. You look like a bean pole; you're losing your figure completely."

"Thanks!"

"Well, look at you. You—"

"Matthew!" Juliet said sternly. "Leave the poor girl alone."

"Someone has to talk some sense into her. She hasn't been out for weeks."

"That's an exaggeration," Stacy told him. "I came to your engagement party last week."

His mouth turned back. "I hardly think a half an hour twirl around the room is putting in a respectable appearance," he said dryly. "You were no sooner there than you had left again."

"But I was there," she insisted.

"For what it was worth. You're becoming a hermit, Stacy."

She hunched her shoulders over. "I go out if I want to."

"And you don't think tonight is important enough to make a special effort?" He was fast running out of patience with her. "This film is your first big break, Stacy, the first time you've had such good billing."

She gave him a mocking smile. "I'm lost among the other small fry, as usual."

Matthew shook his head. "Not this time. You're way up there with the stars."

She looked stunned. "I don't understand."

"You're perfect in the part of Kate," Juliet put in gently. "You deserve the honor."

Jake has said Kate was perfect—she wouldn't think of Jake! "I'm surprised Paul Forbes allowed it."

"He didn't have any say in it. Weston insisted on it, and when he insists like that no one argues with him." Matthew watched Stacy closely for her reaction.

Her face paled, her breathing shallow. She licked her bottom lip, a purely nervous gesture. "Jake did?" she asked shakily.

"*Jake* did," Matthew confirmed.

"But I— Why?"

He shrugged. "Who can tell why that man does anything? He just does it."

Juliet gave her a gentle smile. "We can wait for you while you change."

It had taken her aback that Jake should do such a thing for her, but it didn't change her decision not to attend the premiere. She didn't want to see Jake and rake up the feelings she still had for him, feelings that she had pushed to the background to stop them hurting so much.

It was four months since she had left the film location, four months of fighting the love she felt for Jake, four months of knowing it was a fight she couldn't possibly win. She had heard nothing from him—and hadn't expected to. As far as she was concerned the break had been final.

But Matthew was right; she was losing her figure, and she would lose her looks, too, if she wasn't careful. It somehow didn't seem to matter any more—the ambition she had always possessed in abundance just not there any more. If she went after a job and got it, that was fine; if she didn't get it, that was fine, too. In actual fact she rarely bothered to go after jobs any more, living off the small amount of money she had managed to save the last couple of years. She would worry about what to do next when the money ran out.

"Jake will be there." She stated the obvious.

"Well, yes," Matthew agreed. "But you don't have to go near him. And there's always the possibility he may not be there. He left the filming before anyone else—some crisis in the States, I think," he told her thoughtfully. "He may still be unavailable."

"And he may not," she shook her head. It wasn't a risk she was prepared to take. "No, I'm sorry. I appreciate your coming around here for me, but I'm not going."

"I think you're a fool." Matthew was angry again. "The quickest way over this thing is to face it head-on. Meet the man and get it over with."

She smiled wanly. "You're probably right." But she knew he wasn't. There was no way out of what she felt for Jake.

"But you don't think so," he realized with a sigh. "Oh, hell, Juliet, talk some sense into her."

"Juliet knows better," Stacy answered for the other girl. "I told you he acted like my older brother," she teased.

Juliet laughed. "Yes. And he's not about to take no for an answer."

Stacy sobered. "But you understand, don't you? You know why I can't go."

"I think so." Her friend nodded.

"Then take this big idiot away and try and explain it to him. You should leave now, anyway; it's getting late."

"You're adamant about not coming?" Matthew demanded.

"Very."

"All right, but don't blame us if everyone wants to know where the new up-and-coming star is. I never thought of you as temperamental, but you're certainly giving a good impression of it."

"Come on, Matthew," his fiancé encouraged, pulling him toward the door. "I'll call you tomorrow, Stacy."

"And tell you how good you were," Matthew muttered as a parting shot.

She was able to relax once more when they had gone. The boring serial that had been showing when they arrived was now replaced by an old film. This one was older than most, the story line almost nonexistent, the dialogue deplorable, the only reason for the film being made at all being that the hero managed to make a constant show of his biceps.

Nevertheless, Stacy watched it, and several other programs that held no interest for her. Sandy came in about twelve-thirty, going straight to her bedroom. Their other two roommates were at an all-night party.

Somewhere between the double late-night bill of horror

films, Stacy somehow managed to fall asleep in the chair.
She woke up to the toneless hum of the television. A glance
at her wristwatch telling her it was almost three o'clock in
the morning. The girls should be back from their party
soon—and she hadn't even been to bed yet!

She rose, still and cold, from the chair to switch off the
television, frozen in the act by the banging on the door.
Helen and Sheila must have forgotten their key. God, with
the noise they were making they were going to wake the
whole building.

Jake stood on the doorstep, swaying unsteadily on his
feet, and if she had changed so had he. He looked terrible,
really haggard. Of course the drink didn't help, the strong
smell of whiskey almost choking her. But it was more than
that; he was much thinner, deep lines of strain etched on
either side of his nose and mouth, his dark hair much too
long and showing more gray at his temples. But it was his
eyes that were the worst, his deep blue eyes that had once
glowed with desire for her now showed only cynicism and
disillusionment.

"My God, Jake," she said chokingly. "Is this any time to
call?"

"What the hell does the time matter?" he rasped. "You
obviously hadn't gone to bed yet."

"Come in, for goodness' sake." She pulled him inside.
"You'll disturb all our neighbors." She watched him as he
weaved his way into the lounge to sit down on the sofa, a
creaking protest coming from the old springs as his weight
descended on them. "You didn't drive here in this state?"
she demanded.

He leaned back against the sofa, his eyes closed. "I got a
taxi," he mumbled.

"But what are you doing here?" She still stood hesitantly
in the doorway.

The blue eyes flickered open. "You weren't at the premiere so I had to come to see you. Why weren't you there?" His words were slurred, even more evidence of his heavy drinking.

"I didn't want to go."

"You didn't want to see me," he mocked.

"You place too much importance on yourself," she retorted heatedly. "I simply didn't feel like going."

"I wanted to see you," he was talking softly, almost as if in conversation with himself. "Did you know that I love you?" he asked matter-of-factly.

Stacy paled, swallowing hard. "Wh—what did you say?"

"I said I—" The room grew suddenly quiet.

Stacy looked at him in horror as she saw his head droop to one side, his deep breathing evidence of his sleeping. She couldn't believe this! Jake had come here at three o'clock in the morning, had calmly told her he loved her, and now he had passed out on the sofa!

CHAPTER TEN

Sandy came into the kitchen yawning tiredly. She was dressed in a long nightshirt and brown mule slippers, her shoulder-length hair permed into a long afro style. She wordlessly poured herself a mug of coffee before sitting down opposite Stacy at the breakfast table.

"The man in the lounge," she said tiredly.

"Mm?" Stacy sipped her own coffee.

"Who is he?"

"Jake Weston."

That brought a slight spark of interest into Sandy's otherwise hazy blue eyes. "The author?"

"Mm." Stacy nodded.

"Oh." Sandy stood up to flip-flop her way back out to the lounge. She was back a few seconds later. "Handsome devil." She sat down again.

"Mm," Stacy said again.

"Does he belong to you?"

"No!"

"No?" Sandy's eyebrows rose, the color of them denoted by her name. "One of the others, then?"

Stacy decided she had better make an effort to explain Jake's presence here, even if she wasn't sure of his reasons herself. "He's here to see me, but he doesn't *belong* to me."

"Well, I didn't mean literally. I'm just not used to finding strange men flaked out on the sofa. Has he been there all night?"

"Since about three," Stacy confirmed.

"And you've been sitting up with him all night." She indicated Stacy's crumpled jeans and jumper.

"I dozed in the chair a bit. But I couldn't just leave him there. He could have wandered into any of your rooms."

Sandy smiled. "I don't think any of us would have minded. I know I wouldn't."

"Maybe that's what I was afraid of," she said dryly.

Sandy stood up. "I'm going back to bed." She refilled her mug with coffee. "Your author was beginning to wake, by the way. I caught a glimpse of deep blue eyes through those marvelous long lashes."

"Oh, God!" Stacy jumped to her feet. "Why didn't you tell me earlier?" she said angrily.

Sandy shrugged. "He was only just beginning to move. Besides, he doesn't look as if he would get very far."

"You're probably right." Stacy remembered his inebriated state of last night and imagined he must have quite a hangover this morning.

By the time the two of them entered the lounge, Jake had managed to pull himself into a sitting position, his eyes still half closed as if in pain. Stacy had removed his shoes the night before and placed a blanket over him, although this had since been pushed off.

"Good morning," Sandy called to him good-naturedly.

"Hi." Jake grimaced at the effort just this little word took, raising his hand to his aching temple. "God, my head hurts!"

Sandy grinned before going into her bedroom and closing the door. Stacy looked at Jake uncertainly. She seemed to have done nothing else but look at him all night, feasting her eyes on him as he slept.

"I'm not surprised," she said unsympathetically.

He blinked to clear his vision, slipping out of his crumpled jacket and releasing his bow tie. "I could use some coffee," he mumbled.

Stacy pointedly sat down, her legs tucked beneath her in the chair. "The kitchen is over there," she said callously, her chin high as she determined not to look at him.

He ran a hand around the back of his stiff neck, a dark growth of beard on his chin. "You won't get me some?"

"I'm not a servant!"

"All right." He stood up wearily, his clothes very creased from his night's sleep in them. "Over there, you said?" .

She could hear him opening and shutting cupboards as he looked for the coffee and a cup to put it in. She felt herself weakening toward him as she heard him swearing softly to himself, feeling guilty as he continued to mutter.

He appeared to have got no further than putting the kettle on by the time she got out there, and pushing him out of the way, she made two fresh cups of coffee. It seemed to be the only thing that was keeping her awake at the moment. She had started to drift off to sleep around six o'clock, but had been woken up again when Helen and Sheila came in from their party.

"Thanks." Jake took a huge gulp of the strong brew. "I guess I must have passed out on you last night."

"You guess right." She carried her own drink through to the lounge and sat down again.

Jake followed her, obviously feeling slightly better after drinking the reviving coffee. "You aren't in a good mood when you wake up."

Her green eyes flashed like emeralds. She was well aware of the picture she must make with her hair tied back untidily and the dark circles around her eyes in her pale face. "*When* I wake up I'm usually in a good mood," she told him sharply. "I don't happen to have just woken up. I've been awake most of the night."

"You have?" He raised dark eyebrows. "I slept very well."

She gave him an angry glare. "Mainly because you were unconscious for most of it."

He slowly put down his empty mug. "Do you think I was drunk last night?" he asked slowly.

She gave a harsh laugh. "I don't think it at all, I know it. You were absolutely stoned when you arrived here, or I would have called a taxi and had you taken to your hotel."

"I wasn't drunk, Stacy," he told her softly. "I'd been on the plane for hours, gone to a premiere it turned out I needn't have attended, and spent two hours at a party that bored the pants off me. I have to admit I had a couple of drinks there, but—"

"A couple!" she snorted her disbelief. "More like a couple of dozen. You arrived on my doorstep at three o'clock in the morning, talked incoherently for several minutes before going unconscious."

Jake came to stand in front of her, his firm muscular thighs on a level with her eyes. "I wasn't drunk, Stacy," he repeated steadily. "I was exhausted. I'd taken a couple of pills to keep me awake and the whiskey on top seemed to put me in a coma. I could feel the effects of it on my way over here, but I had to see you. And I don't think I was talking incoherently at all. I seem to remember I told you I love you."

Color flared into her otherwise pale cheeks. "The ramblings of a drunken man don't mean a lot to me."

"I wasn't drunk, damn you!" His fingers bit into the soft flesh at the top of her arms as he pulled her to her feet. He held her immobile against the stirring of his thighs, his head bent on a level with her own. "I love you, Stacy. I love you!" He shook her roughly.

She took a deep breath. "And when did you make this

startling discovery?'' She had to scorn him or she would simply have melted against the urgency of his body, not caring what he felt for her as long as he made love to her. She closed her eyes against the total maleness of him, fighting the betrayal of her own body.

"It wasn't startling at all," he contradicted gently. "I've known for a very long time."

She couldn't believe him, she *wouldn't* believe him. He was playing some new game with her—and she wasn't going to play. "Really?" she said disinterestedly.

"What the hell is the matter with you?" he rasped angrily, shaking her once again. "What's happened to you?"

She wrenched away from him. *He* was what had happened to her, him and the love she felt toward him, the love that was slowly destroying her. "There's nothing wrong with me, I just don't understand your reasons for being here."

"Don't understand.... Haven't I just been telling you?" He sounded exasperated. "Or do you have men making those sort of declarations every day, so that it means nothing to you if one more fool does it? Oh, hell!" He ran a hand roughly through his dark hair. "I didn't come here with the intention of throwing out this sort of insults."

She hadn't flinched at his barb, expecting it as a mouse expects torment from a cat. "Why did you come here?" she asked dully.

"To tell you I love you!" He searched her cold, hard features, shaking his head dazedly. "It doesn't seem to mean much to you."

She could have told him that nothing seemed to mean much to her lately, nothing seemed to break through the numbness and depression she felt. She loved this man and he said he loved her, and yet she knew there could never be any happiness for them together. Apart from him she was barely alive, but if she accepted the little he was prepared to give she would be subjecting herself to a living hell. This man had no trust in any woman, and it would destroy her in the end.

"I'm flattered, of course—"

"Flattered!" he cut in angrily. "I don't want you to be *flattered*, for God's sake! I want to know how you feel about me."

"I feel nothing for you," she lied.

His face darkened with anger. "I wouldn't say the way you tremble against me was nothing," he snapped.

Stacy sighed. "I'll admit to a certain amount of physical attraction."

"You'll admit to a damn sight more than that!" he said grimly, making a threatening move toward her.

"No!" She backed away. "Please, remember where you are. I have three roommates, any one of which could come out here at any moment."

"But they won't," he said with a certainty that surprised her. "Not if they have any sense. I wouldn't like them to be embarrassed."

Stacy fought against him as he pulled her effortlessly into his arms, trying to evade his searching mouth, but knowing the temptation to feel the full possession of this man, to just once be wholly his.

His mouth was gentle on hers, his hands beneath her sweater as he strained her against the hard throbbing of his thighs. "Kiss me, Stacy. I *need* you to," he groaned.

She couldn't resist his pleadings and her mouth flowered beneath his as she felt him deepen the kiss. They lay side by side on the sofa, Jake's shirt completely unbuttoned, her sweater pushed up so that their naked torsos molded together. She hadn't been able to say no as he had kissed and caressed her, and she wished now that they were completely alone in the apartment so that their consummation could be complete.

"Your body is beautiful," Jake groaned against one rosy nipple, smoothing her skin with trembling passion. "I want to love you," he rasped. "All of you."

"I know, I know," she moaned her own pleasure. "Oh, Jake, why did you have to leave me?"

"You left me." His mouth teased her breasts to full pulsating life. "I asked you to stay; I almost begged you."

"And you know the reason I couldn't." She lay weak and pliant in his arms. "I don't want to be your mistress, Jake. I just don't want that." And yet she knew that if he chose to take her right now that's exactly what she would become.

"I'm not asking it, you silly child," he chided gently. "I want you to marry me."

"No!" She pushed against his chest. "You... you can't mean that."

He held her easily beneath him. "Why can't I?"

"Because I— You don't want to get married, not after— not after Margaret."

Her words curtailed his ardor, and swinging his legs to the floor he began to button his shirt. "Do you know why I was originally late on the film set?"

She shrugged. "Something held you up in America, something personal."

"Very personal," he acknowledged grimly. "Margaret killed herself just before I was due to leave."

"Oh, no!" She could see how affected he had been by his wife's death. "I didn't know," she said gently.

"I was planning to divorce her at the time. Oh, not that she knew about that, it was still just an idea. She didn't kill herself on purpose, she just took one pill too many on top of one drink too many." He turned to look at Stacy's hand as it rested on his thigh, picking it up to kiss her palm with probing lips. "And then I came to England and met you, fell in love with you—and all you seemed to be doing was pushing your other men down my throat."

She hung her head. "You said I reminded you of your wife."

"Under great provocation."

"Perhaps. But—"

"You're nothing like her, nothing at all! Will you please marry me, Stacy?"

She took a deep breath to answer no, but the words wouldn't come. She wanted to be his wife, wanted that above all things. How marvelous to wake up in the morning and find Jake beside her for the rest of her life, to know he was her husband, this marvelous, fascinating man that she loved—her own husband. But the reasons for her leaving him in Cornwall still applied: his terrible temper when he thought her interested in another man.

She stood up, wringing her hands together as he watched her, a completely vulnerable expression on his usually arrogant features. "It wouldn't work," she said evasively.

Instantly he was on his feet in front of her. "Why wouldn't it? You know everything about me that could possibly harm any marriage we have. Brad told me that he had explained to you about Danny and Margaret."

She smoothed his furrowed brow. "I was so sorry to hear about your son. He would have been my age by now."

He shrugged. "I loved him, but it hit Margaret much harder than it hit me. I'm convinced that after he died she was on a course of self-destruction she just didn't want to stop. Why wouldn't *our* marriage work, Stacy? Am I so unlovable?"

"No," she admitted shakily. "Far from it."

"Then why?" He tenderly touched her cheek. "I love you, I want to marry you. What more can I say?"

She shook her head. "Absolutely nothing. And don't think I'm not grateful for your love, but I—"

He shook her roughly. "Will you stop using words like grateful and flattered," he said disgustedly. "I want you for my wife. It would work between us, I'm convinced of it."

"It may do, until your next flare-up of jealous temper."

He turned away. "So that's it. I can't help my jealousy where you're concerned. It rises up like a red tide and takes over."

"I know."

"But that's only because I'm so uncertain about you," he explained pleadingly. "God, you led me to believe it was Day you really wanted, and I still believed it until I saw him with Juliet last night. They told me they're getting married soon."

"That's right."

"Was everything you said about him a lie?"

She gave him a startled look. "Everything?"

"You know what you implied that last day in Cornwall, you wanted me to think he was your lover. But you're innocent, aren't you?" he probed.

"Innocent?"

"A virgin."

"Not in thought." How many times had she imagined being made fully his!

"But in body," he insisted.

"And if I wasn't?" she challenged.

"Then I'd still want you. You're like a fever in my blood."

"That doesn't change anything. If I married you I would only have to look at another man to know the cruel edge of your tongue."

"That's only because I love you." He sounded agonized.

"But you've been like this from the start, ever since we first met."

"Because I loved you even then. I once told you to imagine I had fallen in love with your screen test. Well, don't imagine it anymore—believe it. That's exactly the way it happened. You're the reason I had finally decided to divorce Margaret, the reason I had to be a free man when I came over to England."

She searched his face for some sign of mockery...and found none. She shook her head. "You have to be joking."

"It's never seemed particularly funny to me. As you know, I insisted choosing the person to play Kate myself. I looked at hundreds of screen tests, some of them good, some of them bad. But as soon as I saw you I seemed to go under. I even had them make up my own personal copy of it. Over the next few months I looked at it constantly, hardly able to believe the way I felt. What I did know was that if you felt the same way about me when we met, then I had to marry you. Thank God I hadn't actually asked Margaret for a divorce before she died; I would have felt as guilty as hell. But when I finally met you...."

"Yes?" she asked breathlessly.

"...You were more beautiful than I even imagined. I had looked at that damn film so many times that when I saw you get in the elevator that day I could hardly believe it was you. The costume was the same, and yet the girl inside it was of this era, a product of this modern permissive society. That was when the jealousy started," he admitted with a sigh.

"Quite unnecessarily."

"Yes," he agreed softly. "But I couldn't seem to stop myself. You have to remember that I lived with Margaret's other men for so long that each man you came into contact with seemed to be a threat to me. That night Forbes tried to force you I felt murderous. And then when he taunted you on the film set! God, I hate his guts!''

"So do most people. But I think his attack on me was partly my own fault. I should never have had dinner with him. I only did it to thwart you.''

"Because you thought I was married.''

"Yes.'' She nodded.

"I don't think I was completely over the shock of Margaret's death; maybe I still felt married. Whatever the reason, you shied away from me completely.

"You had lied about your identity,'' she reminded. "I found that unforgivable.''

"Yes. I had seen you on film, but I couldn't get to know the real you that way. I had no way of knowing whether my being Jake Weston would make any difference to how you felt about me.''

"Make me more interested, you mean,'' she said dryly.

He grimaced. "That backfired on me, too. After that you seemed to find every other man in the vicinity worthy of your notice but treated me with contempt. I could have killed Forbes at the time, but in a way his treatment of you enabled me to get close to you again. My offer to keep other men at bay seemed a good idea at the time.''

"Until you saw me kiss Matthew, a purely brotherly kiss, I might add. After that I needed protection from you. You . . . you almost—''

"Almost took you as brutally as Forbes tried to do. Yes,'' he admitted with a deep sigh. "I couldn't control my feelings for you any longer. In some ways you seemed to be everything I had ever wanted, and yet I couldn't reconcile myself to the fact that some other man had taken you first. I've never thought of myself as a possessive man—With Margaret as an example, I couldn't be—but to think of other men touching *your* body, loving you the way *I* wanted to, knowing every delicious inch of you . . . ." He shuddered. "I couldn't take that. And then you told me I would be the first!"

"And you didn't believe me."

"But I wanted to! You'll never know how badly I wanted to believe that."

"I almost told you how much I loved you that night, but you misunderstood me again and thought I was going to say I loathed men."

He came toward her like a man in a trance. "You love me?" he asked disbelievingly.

Too late she realized she had given herself away. There would be no turning back now, Jake wouldn't let her go. "But it still wouldn't work, Jake." She backed away from him. "I won't become a prisoner of your love. I have friends, male friends—not lovers," she added hastily. "And I'm not about to give them up."

"Tell me you love me." He seemed not to have heard her impassioned pleadings. "Oh, *God*, Stacy, tell me you love me!"

The agony in his voice was her undoing. "I love you, Jake. Oh, yes, I love you" She went willingly into his arms, longing for the feel of his lips on hers, for the full arousal she could instantly feel in him.

They were hungry for each other, their kisses heated, their caresses fevered. Jake was shaking by the time they drew apart, his breathing ragged as he fought for the control that neither of them seemed able to regain.

"Marry me, Stacy," he groaned. "Please!"

"But your jealousy—"

"We'll have to fight that together. I'm warning you that if you don't soon say yes I'm going to make love to you right here and now, regardless of your roommates."

"Perhaps if we just became lovers that would be best for both of us."

He looked angry. "What do you mean?"

"Affairs aren't as difficult to end as marriages," she said softly, evading his searching gaze. "My way you could be free any time you wanted to be."

"I don't want to be free ever again. I can assure you that I've never been in love before, my marriage to Margaret was a mistake from start to finish. I know I've been unreasonable with you, but I love you so much, and I want to marry you. I want you for all time, Stacy."

He had used that word to her so many times before and yet she knew that this time he meant it in a different way. The wanting was his way of loving, of needing—and she could deny him no longer.

"And my work?"

"I won't stop you from doing anything you want to do."

She was aware that at this moment he would deny her nothing, and she didn't like his vulnerability. "And children?"

"Only if you want them."

"Oh, I want them, but do you?"

"My child growing inside you," he said huskily, wonderingly. "Oh, yes. And it will be a beautiful daughter with her mother's glorious red hair and sparkling green eyes."

"Or a son with his father's arrogance and charm?"

He laughed softly. "Do I have charm?"

"When you want to have."

"And is my charm working now? Are you going to marry me?" The lines of strain at his nose and mouth were back again, evidence of his tension. "Can you bear to live with a man who loves you so much it's almost made him crazy with jealousy?"

"I can, as long as he never forgets that I love him in return."

"You'll never regret it," he promised as he once more claimed her lips.

She hoped she wouldn't, but there was still that vague feeling of unease at the back of her mind.

THEY WERE MARRIED three weeks later, their honeymoon one of idyllic love on one of the Greek islands. Stacy had to admit to a certain amount of tension on their wedding night, but Jake had not hurried her at all, introducing her to all the pleasures of her body with a gentleness that had finally taken her by storm.

After that night they had become slaves to the desire that engulfed them whenever their eyes happened to meet, the time of day and place seeming unimportant. They lived in a hazy world of eating, sleeping and making love, the outside world forgotten by both of them.

The four-week honeymoon almost over, they had to begin to think of returning to the day-to-day pressures that still frightened Stacy whenever she thought about them. Here at the villa they had lived a solitary existence, needing no one but each other, but once they were back among other people she had no idea of Jake's reaction.

They would be flying straight to the house that had been prepared for them in the States, Stacy deciding to end her career rather than risk being away from Jake for weeks on end. She knew he was relieved by her decision, but he had in no way tried to influence her either way. In actual fact she had received many offers of work, the reviews of her acting in the film bringing her many offers from people who once wouldn't even have considered her.

But marriage couldn't be made to work with the couple constantly apart, and anyway, she wanted to be with Jake. His main work was done in America, but he traveled a great deal for his research, and she wanted to go with him, beginning to know some of that jealousy herself that he possessed in too great a quantity.

He was up in the villa now making telephone calls, only two days of their honeymoon left, and the thought of returning to work was beginning to become a reality. They were business calls, and so Stacy had opted to go down to the beach and sunbathe. Jake would join her when he had finished.

She felt the heat of the sun on her back momentarily blotted out and felt the familiar rise of pleasure that Jake's presence always gave her. "Hello, darling," she murmured sleepily. "Would you rub some oil on my back for me?"

She had undone the single back-fastening of her bikini top and squirmed with pleasure as she felt the soothing oil being smoothed into her golden skin. Then she knew only panic, her husband's touch a familiar and intimate thing to her—and this wasn't Jake!

She rolled over, clutching her loosened top to her to stare into the pair of twinkling brown eyes that belonged to a boy she had never seen before. She struggled into a sitting position, glaring at the intruder.

"You have to be English," he said with satisfaction. "I'm from Scotland myself."

Stacy gave him a chilling smile, longing to do up the fastening of her bikini top, but unable to do so with one hand. And she didn't dare let go of the front—it was the only thing keeping her decent. "How nice for you," she said sarcastically. "Did you know this is a private beach?"

He shrugged, a boy of her own age, quite handsome in a youthful way, dressed only in a pair of cutoff Levis. "I often come along here in my spare time. I work at one of the hotels farther along the coast."

"Yes, well...." She held onto her dignity with effort, her

face fiery red. Couldn't he see how uncomfortable she felt sitting here clutching her bikini top! If only he would go away and let her get dressed. If Jake should come out here now.... She shied away from the thought, envisaging the shortest marriage in history. "This is a private beach and I think you should leave now."

"Why?"

"Because—"

"Because her husband may not like you being here," Jake drawled from behind them.

Stacy looked up in dismay, trying hard to gauge his mood, but his face was closed to her. Oh, God, no! She closed her eyes, feeling the happiness and well-being drain out of her. Not now, she couldn't lose him now, and all through a misunderstanding.

"I didn't realize you were married." The young boy looked at her almost accusingly.

Jake came down on the sand beside her, dressed in navy blue swimming trunks, his body deeply tanned. "She doesn't look old enough, does she?" he agreed mildly, pushing her hand away to fasten her top. "Let me, darling. I've warned you about sunbathing like this."

"Yes, Jake." She searched his face for his reaction, but he turned away from her.

"Oh, well." The boy stood up, obviously deciding to cut his losses. "I suppose I'd better get back to work. Nice meeting you." He waved before leaving.

To Stacy the silence between herself and Jake was oppressive. God, what an end to a honeymoon—the end of the marriage. She watched as Jake stretched out on the sand beside her, his hands behind his head as pillows, his eyes closed.

"Jake...." she broached tentatively.

"Mm?" He didn't move.

"Jake, are you angry?"

His eyes flickered open at that. "Should I be?"

"Well, no. But—"

His eyes closed again. "Then I'm not."

"But—"

He jackknifed into a sitting position, all calm leaving him now. "I'm trying very hard not to lose my temper, Stacy," he said through gritted teeth. "Look at this." He held out his hands and she could see that they were shaking. "I came out of the villa to see that kid sitting on the beach with you, touching you as he rubbed oil on your back, and the old red ride passed in front of my eyes. I wanted to storm down here and beat hell out of him."

"But you didn't."

"No." Some of the tension seemed to leave his body. "I stayed up there for several minutes longer. I thought of the way we make love, the way you give yourself absolutely to me, the way you hold nothing back, and I knew that whatever that kid was doing here on our beach you were not encouraging him."

"Oh, Jake." Tears shone in her eyes "I thought he was you. I nearly died when I realized he wasn't. And then I thought—then I thought you—"

"You thought I would come down here and go berserk," he finished for her, gently wiping away her tears. "And I very nearly did."

"But you didn't, that's the main thing."

"Mm, I suppose it's a start."

It was more than that to her. She knew now that whatever pressures did lie ahead of them, together they would be able to work them out. Their love meant more to them than Jake's jealousy ever would, and he would learn to control that, too, in time.

Jake picked her up in his arms and began to stride back toward the villa with her.

"What are you doing?" she gasped.

"The honeymoon isn't over yet." He smiled down at her. "And I intend putting my brand of possession on you once again."

"Oh, Jake," she giggled.

He lay down with her on the huge double bed they had shared the last few weeks, taking off her bikini with a familiarity that still had the power to make her blush. He devoured her body, his lips making her squirm with pleasure. "I don't think the honeymoon will ever be over for us," he moaned throatily, kicking off the navy blue swimming trunks, the last piece of clothing to separate their naked bodies. "Oh, love me, Stacy. Love me!"

This was where she belonged, where she would always belong. She cried her love for him as the waves of desire washed over them both, taking them to the heights.

WHAT READERS SAY ABOUT
HARLEQUIN SUPERROMANCE #1

End of Innocence
by Abra Taylor

"I am impatiently awaiting the
next Superromance."
J.D.,* Sandusky, Ohio

"I couldn't put it down!"
M.M., North Baltimore, Ohio

"Just great – I can't wait until
the next one."
R.M., Melbourne, Florida

"I *loved* it!"
A.C., Pailin, New Jersey

"I enjoyed *End of Innocence*
by Abra Taylor so much."
J L., Greenville, South Carolina

*Names available on request.

HARLEQUIN SUPERROMANCE

A timely new series of contemporary
love stories! Longer, exciting, sensual and
dramatic, these compelling new books are
for you—the woman of today.

Complete and mail the coupon on the
following page now and receive
these first two exciting new
HARLEQUIN SUPERROMANCE titles!

HARLEQUIN SUPERROMANCE #1

END OF INNOCENCE by Abra Taylor

They called him El Sol, golden-haired star of the bullring.
Liona was proud and happy to be his fiancée...until
a tragic accident threw her to the mercies of El Sol's
forbidding brother, a man who despised Liona almost
as much as he wanted her....

HARLEQUIN SUPERROMANCE #2

LOVE'S EMERALD FLAME by Willa Lambert

The steaming jungle of Peru was the stage for their
love. Diana Green, a spirited and beautiful young
journalist, who became a willing pawn in a dangerous
game...and Sloane Hendriks, a lonely desperate man
driven by a secret he would reveal to no one.

HARLEQUIN SUPERROMANCE

A Contemporary Love Story

Complete and mail this coupon today!

Harlequin Reader Service

In U.S.A.
MPO Box 707
Niagara Falls, NY 14302

In Canada
649 Ontario St.
Stratford, Ont. N5A 6W2

Please send me END OF INNOCENCE,
HARLEQUIN SUPERROMANCE #1. I am enclosing my
check or money order for $2.25 for each copy ordered.

Number of copies _____ @ $2.25 each
= $_____

Please send me LOVE'S EMERALD FLAME,
HARLEQUIN SUPERROMANCE #2. I am enclosing my
check or money order for $2.25 for each copy ordered.

Number of copies _____ @ $2.25 each
= $_____

Total $_____

N.Y. and Ariz. residents add appropriate sales
tax $_____

Postage and handling $___.59___

Final total $_____

I enclose _____
(Please send check or money order. We cannot be responsible for
cash sent through the mail.)
Prices subject to change without notice.

NAME_____
(Please Print)
ADDRESS_____

CITY_____

STATE/PROV _____ ZIP/POSTAL CODE_____

Offer expires May 31, 1981

101563123